ENEMY OR FRIEND?

This book is dedicated to the slave workers who suffered and died in the Occupation of the Channel Islands during the Second World War.

This is the account of my childhood, long ago, during the German Occupation of Guernsey. At that time I imagined carrying out a daring rescue, but in reality this proved impossible. I have, however, woven this dream into my story.

Lyn Renouf Edwards

ENEMY OR FRIEND?

Published in 2009 by
Channel Island Publishing

CHANNEL
ISLAND
PUBLISHING

Unit 3B, Barette Commercial Centre
La Route du Mont Mado
St John, Jersey, JE3 4DS
Tel (01534) 860806
www.channelislandpublishing.com

ISBN 978-1-905095-28-5

Printed by Cromwell Press Group, Trowbridge, Wiltshire.

ENEMY OR FRIEND?

For Kate, Alex, William and Thomas

ILLUSTRATIONS

I acknowledge with thanks, permission to reproduce photographs in this book provided by:

Guernsey Occupation Museum
Festung Guernsey
Channel Island Occupation Society
Carol Toms collection
R. Blanchford collection
The Guernsey Press
The Guernsey Brewery
V. Edwards
S. Galliford

ACKNOWLEDGEMENTS:

Grateful thanks for the help so generously given:
Richard Heaume. Guernsey Occupation Museum
Paul Bourgaize. Festung Guernsey
The Channel Island Occupation Society
Maggie Falla and staff at Guille-Allès Library
Staff at Priaulx Library
Lynne Ashton. Guernsey Museum
Also patience, help and forbearance of: M.Edwards, S.Galliford, S.Hamon, M.Lanyon, C.Stubbs, S.Watkins and the Settlement Writers.

Contents

HOW DID IT ALL BEGIN?

Hiding behind the curtains we peered into the garden; in the moonlight the bushes cast long shadows, then out of the blackness two figures emerged, moving slowly, and cautiously towards the house.

One figure was holding something in his hand. As the moon shone there was the glint of metal. It was an axe. For months I'd had nightmares just like this, and woken up terrified, but this wasn't a dream, it was really happening.

The evening had begun like all the others, Mum and I sitting by the dying embers of the fire, alone in the house.

As the room became colder and colder Mum said, "We'll go to bed early tonight, it will be warmer there, but first we must make everything secure."

She lit the candle, and made certain that the front and back doors were locked and bolted. In each room she reached up to make certain that the catches on the windows were firmly in place. As we went out of each room she carefully locked the door, placing a wedge underneath, so it couldn't be opened from outside

Walking upstairs the candle flame flickered, making wavering shadows on the walls, and the darkness seemed to swallow us up. When we went into the bedroom Mum locked the door, and pushed a wedge underneath. I looked around, we should be safe here; every door locked, and all our food was in the wardrobe, hidden away from thieves.

Now was the time of greatest danger, when in the darkness starving men roamed the island, desperate in their search for food; attacking anyone who tried to stop them. People had been badly injured, and some murdered.

As I blew out the candle, Mum opened the curtains, and then we climbed into bed, cuddling up for warmth. Mum told stories of times long ago, when there was enough food so that no one was hungry, and there were shops where you could buy new clothes and shoes. Then the best stories, about having picnics on the beach when there weren't any mines or bombs.

I drifted off to sleep, but suddenly woke up and asked, "Is it morning yet?"

"Not yet, it's curfew time, the middle of the night," replied Mum.

The moon was bright, but there were clouds black against the sky outlined in silver. The room was in darkness for a few minutes, then, as the clouds drifted across, the sky suddenly illuminated with light.

It was warm and comfortable in bed as we snuggled up. Then there was the unmistakeable creak of the garden gate, and the sound of a footstep on gravel. We lay motionless, hardly breathing; but my heart was pounding.

Cautiously we slid out of bed, and crept to the window, there were two men. We knew that they were Germans or Russians, driven by hunger, willing to risk their lives for food.

They drew nearer and nearer, until they were directly under the bedroom window. There was no one to help us; all we had was a German Police whistle, given to us by a German soldier, a man whom most of the islanders thought of as an enemy.

When he found out that we were usually alone in the house he gave us the whistle, and said, " If you are in danger blow hard, and help will arrive."

The men paused, and then one raised his hand towards the window. There was a sharp sound of breaking glass. At the same moment Mum opened the window and blew the whistle. The noise was loud and shrill, penetrating the darkness. The two figures turned, running across the grass and gravel, flinging open the gate, and disappearing into the blackness.

Once more the night was still. We waited, but no one came to investigate what had happened. Returning to bed shivering, we lay close together; Mum's arms were tight around me, and eventually we fell sleep.

As dawn was breaking I woke up, now even more aware than ever of the danger surrounding us. There had been a time when nothing seemed to change, and we were not frightened about what was going to happen next. The more I thought about this it was clear that was a long time ago, when I was quite small, and before the arrival of Jacques.

DANGER
Chapter 1

There was a time when I wasn't really frightened of anything. Well, I probably wasn't too keen on spiders, and I didn't like the dark, but I didn't know what fear was.

It all began to change on the day Dad said, "We've got to go and get gas masks."

"Why?" I asked.

"Well, people say there may be a war, and if there is, enemy planes could come and drop poisoned gas. The masks will keep us safe."

The masks were horrible; mine squashed my face. It was very hot to wear, and smelt of rubber. Looking out of the front everything looked misty. The masks seemed to have snouts, like pigs, through which the air entered.

You must remember that I was quite little then, and when I had it on there was the sound of breathing; and I wasn't sure if it was me, or someone, or something, that might get me.

The very worst thing about the masks, and the most frightening, was that when they put them on Mum and Dad didn't look like Mum and Dad any more, they looked like monsters.

Mum tried to be reassuring, "Don't be silly, we're just like the three bears, with a small mask, a middle sized mask and a big one."

That didn't make a scrap of difference.

The masks were in boxes with strings so you carried them on your

A gas mask similar to the one worn by Marianne.

shoulder. We took them everywhere at first, but when nothing happened we left them hanging on a peg in the hall,

"We'll use them when we need to," said Dad.

At first everything went on as usual. Most days we went to Moulin Huet beach, and ate picnics, built castles, paddled and swam in the sea.

Then one afternoon, just a few weeks later, Mum and Dad hurried me out of the house and we set off to Westwood, which was the big house where Dad's Mother and Father lived.

Walking along the lanes was strange; there were no other people to be seen. "Where's everyone?" I asked.

Mum looked anxious, "They're all indoors waiting for the news, waiting to see if there's going to be a war."

When we arrived at Westwood no one smiled. We all went into the dining room, and sat around the table.

"The B.B.C. broadcast will begin in a moment," said Dad, turning on the wireless set.

There was the sound Big Ben in London chiming eleven times. Everyone sat so still it seemed as if they'd been turned into statues.

A solemn voice began to speak, it was the Prime Minister. He said that the Germans, and their leader Adolf Hitler, knew that if they didn't stop fighting the people in Poland, and begin to start taking their soldiers out of the country by eleven o'clock, Britain and Germany would be at war.

He said, "No such undertaking has been received, and that consequently this country is at war with Germany."

The quietness in the room was terrifying, then Grandmamma started to cry. For the first time I knew grown-ups could be as frightened as children.

JACQUES
Chapter 2

The days passed and nothing happened, then one morning I woke up early and looked out of the bedroom window. The sun was shining, and the leaves of the trees in the lane were turning golden and brown; some were fluttering and spinning in the breeze as they fell to the ground.

Then, to my amazement, a boy appeared in the garden of the stone house that joined on to our cottage. He started jumping over plants, and running around the bushes.

Who was he? Mrs Le Marquand, who lived in the house, didn't seem to like children very much; she always frowned and looked cross if I walked onto her path.

"Marianne, breakfast's ready," Mum called, and I ran down.

"Do you know there's a boy next door, and he's playing in the garden?"

"Yes I do. He's called Jacques. Mrs Le Marquand is his Grandmother. She went across to France to bring him back to Guernsey. Now there's a war his Mum and Dad think that the German armies might attack France. They think there'll be fighting, and Jacques will be safe here."

That was scary, if Jacques had to escape from France that meant that the war was coming near, because on a fine day you can see the coast of France.

"Germans won't come to Guernsey, will they?" I asked.

"Course not," laughed Mum, "why would Hitler want to bother with a little island?

Let's have breakfast and afterwards, because Mrs. Le Marquand has a lot to do, we'll ask if Jacques can spend the day with us. You can play together, it may be a bit difficult because he can't speak English."

11

I wasn't too sure about this idea, but Mrs. Le Marquand seemed delighted, and Jacques followed us back.

He didn't look like a Guernsey boy, his hair was cut differently, he had longer trousers, and when he started speaking I didn't understand one word.

I decided the best idea was to show him around the garden. As we walked past the pump, where we got all our water, I lifted the handle and pushed it up and down. It was hard work, but soon the water gushed out over the stones and ferns around the edge, and the drops shone like diamonds.

Jacques picked up the bucket and placed it under the spout and pumped, and the water splashed and danced as it fell.

The bucket was very heavy, and we carried it between us to the back door.

"Well you've saved me one job," Mum said smiling," I'm doing some baking, would you like to help?"

I nodded, and we went into the kitchen. Our kitchen was best in winter, always warm and cosy, but in summer it did get a bit hot.

As it was baking day the fire in the black-leaded range, where Mum did all the cooking was bright red, so the oven at the side was very hot. The range burnt coal and wood, and Mum put on a shovel full of coal, filled the kettle, lifted off the cover on the top of the range, and put the kettle over the fire.

Then we all set to work. Mum made some pies, while we made men with the leftover pastry; they had currants for the eyes and buttons, and sultanas for mouths.

While everything was cooking, the bowl was filled with hot water from the kettle, and Mum washed up, while we dried the dishes.

Soon the kitchen was full of delicious smells, and my mouth was watering. When Mum returned from throwing the water away in the garden, the pastry men came out of the oven.

She suggested that we had elevenses sitting on the steps in the garden. We each had a pastry man, and glasses of the icy-cold water from the pump.

It seemed a good time to teach Jacques English. I pointed at the glass, saying, "Glass." Then at everything around us saying the words. Jacques didn't say anything, he just grinned.

Just then my cat, Tibby Puss, came and rubbed against our legs purring, so I tried again, "Cat."

Jacques said, "Le chat."

So then I pointed at myself, and said, "Marianne," then at him and said, "Jacques," last of all at the cat, and said, "Tibby Puss."

Jacques grinned, then repeated, "Tibby Puss," so I clapped.

When we'd finished we explored the garden; it was full of flowers, bushes, trees, little paths, and stone steps winding from one part to another up to a field.

After exploring it was nearly dinnertime, and we ran down towards the cottage. At the top of the steps we came to the little path that lead to the lavatory.

Now here was a problem, what should it be called?

It's strange that the lavatory had so many different names. Some people called it the privy. Mum called it the lavvy; Dad the lav, which Mum said was common. Grandmamma called it the water closet, which was even stranger because there wasn't any water, and other people called it the W.C. for short.

Every week Mum cut squares of newspaper, and put them on a hook on the wall, so we could wipe our bottoms. Then she scrubbed the seat, but the lavvy always had a peculiar smell.

We walked to the door and Jacques wrinkled his nose. It's lucky he hasn't been here when the cesspit underneath is full, I thought. When it was full Dad had to empty it with a bucket, and then carry the bucket to pits he dug in the field at the top of the garden.

When he did that we closed all the windows and doors, but soon the house was full of the awful noxious smell, that lingered for ages.

Jacques must have wanted to go, because he went in and closed the door. When he came out I said, "Lavvy," then I went in, and heard Mum calling out that dinner was ready.

We had meat pie and rice pudding, that had been cooked in the morning. Dad asked if Jacques had learnt any English, and I said, "Tibby Puss."

"Tibby Puss; Cat; Lavvy; Marianne; Thank you," Jacques said.

"Well, that's a good start," said Dad, "have you learnt any French Marianne?"

"Le chat," I said tentatively, " which I think means the cat," and Dad nodded.

After we'd finished eating we went out again. First we had turns on the swing hanging from a branch. Then we climbed high up on the big oak tree. I climbed as high as Jacques, which was higher than ever before. We played tag, and hide and seek. Whenever we stopped for a rest Tibby Puss wandered over, and Jacques sat holding and stroking him, while Tibs purred more and more loudly.

The shadows were quite long when Mrs Le Marquand came to say it was time for tea.

Jacques called out "Grandmère," and was talking in French all the way home. I wished we could understand what he was saying.

By now it was getting dark so we switched on the electric light. It still seemed magic, because we'd only had electricity for a few months, before that there were oil lamps and candles.

Even better, we now had a wireless set. Mum and Dad were always listening to news about the war, but what was really good were the music and songs, and best of all was Children's Hour, with stories and plays.

After tea, as it was Saturday, it was bath night for every one. On the other days we washed in a bowl in the kitchen.

Dad brought in the little bath from the washhouse, and poured in saucepans of hot water, and when the temperature was right I climbed into the bath and sat down.

Dad came past and rubbed soap on his hands and blew enormous bubbles. Then came the hateful moment when Mum knelt down, and poured cupfuls of water over my head. Then she got the soap, and rubbed it vigorously until there was lots of lather, and started shampooing. Even with the flannel held tight over my eyes it still stung, and the soap got into my mouth.

Next came the "whoosh" of clean water from a jug. When all the soap was rinsed away I clambered out, and was wrapped up in a warm, cuddly towel that smelt of lavender.

Dad was busy carrying the bath outside, and then there was a splash as the water was emptied We could hear him carrying the big tin bath into the kitchen, and filling it up with buckets of hot water from the copper outside ready for his and Mum's bath.

He was grumbling away, "Bath night's balony hard work," as we were settling down for the bedtime story.

That night it was 'Wind In The Willows,' and the chapter where Toad dressed up as a washerwoman, when he escaped from prison.

As we were going upstairs there was the sound of rain, and I was really glad that we didn't have to go out to the lavvy in the night; we had chamber pots under our beds. Mine was white enamel, with a blue rim. Mum and Dad had a posh china pot with red roses. It was Grandmamma who said chamber pot. I called it a po-po. I laughed when rude children said po, or jerry.

After Mum had gone downstairs I listened to the rain, and the splashing of the stream on its way to the sea, and thought about the day. It was good having Jacques next door, and I wondered if we would become friends, and maybe have some adventures.

The cottage where Marianne lived in Moulin Huet Valley.

WESTWOOD
Chapter 3

The next day was Sunday, and we saw Jacques and Grandmère walking down the path. "They're going to the Catholic Church," Mum said. "This afternoon we'll ask if Jacques can come with us to Westwood."

I didn't think Grandmamma would like that very much. She always said boys were noisy dirty creatures, usually up to no good. Poor old Dad, he couldn't have had much fun when he was little.

When we arrived at Westwood there was a lot of wiping of feet on the mat, because Grandmamma became very angry if there was dirt anywhere in the house.

Grandmamma and Grandpa came into the hall, and stared at Jacques, and Grandmamma frowned.

"This is Jacques Le Marquand," said Dad, "he's come from France to live with his Grandmother."

"Welcome to Guernsey," Grandpa said, as he walked over and shook Jacques's hand.

I liked Grandpa, he was quite short, with silver hair, a tickly moustache, and eyes that twinkled when he smiled. Grandmamma was taller, and hardly ever smiled.

She looked at me, " You can both go to the attic to play, but don't make a mess."

Westwood was much bigger than our cottage, but not nearly as cosy. I decided to show Jacques around.

First we went to the kitchen, where there was a gas cooker, and a sink with taps and a plughole. I took some currents out of the jar, closing it carefully so no one would know that any had gone, and we ate them as we went into the hall to the drawing room.

I looked around before opening the door, because I was only allowed to go there with Grandmamma to clean and polish. The room was used at Christmas, or when company came.

We went in, and when the door was firmly closed I took a deep breath; there was the beeswax smell of polish, and everything was gleaming and shining. We looked at the ornaments. Jacques took down a figure of a fisher boy, and I imagined Grandmamma's horrified face if she had seen what he was doing.

After we'd played with all the things that were not supposed to be touched we crept to the door, and cautiously opened it and went upstairs.

I proudly showed Jacques the bathroom with a real bath and washbasin, and flushed the lavatory so the water gushed down, and wished and wished we could do that at home.

We had a quick peep into each of the three bedrooms; they were full of large shiny furniture, and gleaming mirrors.

Next we came to the best part of the house, through the little door in the corner of the landing, and climbed up the steep stairs into the attics. This is where I spent most of my time, and where Grandmamma and Grandpa hardly ever came.

I opened cupboards and took out Dad's collection of soldiers he had when he was a boy, and Jacques arranged them in formation. It seemed as if he'd play with them forever, but I put them away and hurried him into the bedroom.

Inside there was a large bed with four brass balls at the corners of the bedstead. I unscrewed them, and put the bedspread over the corners, and put the balls back. It made a good tent, Jacques immediately dived under, and then came out laughing. Next he lay on the top, as if in a hammock. I was going to get on too when Grandpa called up the stairs, "Come and have a drink, and some cake."

Quick as lightning we unscrewed the balls, and folded the bedspread so Grandmamma wouldn't see the creases.

We hurried down. When we came to the big curving polished banisters Jacques climbed on, and whizzed down to the hall. I followed; it was wonderful. We ran up and slid down again and again.

Suddenly the dining room door opened and Grandmamma stood there with a face as black as thunder.

"What do you think you're doing, you little hooligans. You will spend the rest of the afternoon where I can see you."

When we went into the dining room, everyone had finished eating. We sat at a corner of the table and Grandpa gave us glasses of milk, and some delicious cakes.

I was pleased it wasn't dinner, because Grandmamma always said, "Waste not, want not," and insisted on a clean plate, even if it was something I hated, like brussel sprouts.

When the table was cleared Grandpa took out the snakes and ladders board. Jacques knew what to do and shook the dice.

I listened to what everyone was saying, and was really pleased that Jacques couldn't understand English.

"The boy's parents were very wise," Grandpa said, "If the Germans invade France, it will be terrifying. Remember in The Great War whole villages were destroyed, and men, women and children killed."

Grandpa had told me about the Great War which happened when Dad was a boy. There were lots of awful stories about terrible things.

"His parents may not survive," he carried on, "but they'll be happy to know he's safe here, away from danger."

They talked and talked until it was time to go home. As we reached our gate Tibby Puss strolled out. Jacques picked him up and stroked him. Tibs purred contentedly.

"I think he's very homesick," Mum said when Jacques had gone home, "and Tibby Puss makes him feel a bit happier."

Tucked up in bed that night I thought how awful it would be to leave home, and Mum and Dad, and have to live in a different country with strangers, and even worse not to understand what they're saying. Poor Jacques.

THE FARM
Chapter 4

"Poor Jacques," Mum said on Saturday, " he's so homesick we'll give him a treat, and go to the farm.""Oh good." I loved the farm where Mum's parents, Mam and Papa Camp, lived.

We set off. I sat on a cushion on the cross bar of Dad's bike, Jacques sat on the carrier of Mum's. It's nearly all up hill to the farm at Pleinmont, so there was a lot of panting and puffing. We had to get off and walked up the steepest slopes.

When we arrived we went into the kitchen and drank glasses of creamy milk.

"Show Jacques around," said Mam, "and collect eggs for tea."

We went into the farmyard. There were the hens and cockerel pecking in the dust. Punch the pony was looking over the gate, and the farm cat was curled up in the sunlight.

In the background was the sound of the pig grunting.

"Cochon," Jacques said, and looked around. He pointed at the sty, "La porcherie."

"Do you have a pig at home?" I asked.

He grinned and nodded. Then I knew he used to live in the country, and guessed he missed the animals almost as much as his Mum and Dad.

Next we went into the barn; the walls had been white-washed, and the loft filled with hay for the animals during the cold winter days.

In winter, when the cows were kept in, I sometimes stayed at the farm for the night. Mam and I got up before dawn to milk them.

She'd light the lantern, and we'd go to the stable. It was always warm, even on the coldest night. When we went in the cows looked around, their brown eyes shining, then they'd moo, it almost seemed as is if they were saying 'Hello."

Mam would hang the lantern on a nail, and the walls were covered in gently moving shadows.

But today was warm and sunny, and winter seemed far away. We walked down the garden, and on the way passed the lavvy.

One day a big boy had told me, "You'd better be careful in there 'cause a rat might come up and bite your bum."

When I told Mum she said, "That's nonsense. Rats never bite bottoms, and only rough boys say bum, that's very, very rude."

All the same, I didn't like going in there after that, perhaps Mum was wrong, and I might be bitten on my bum. Even worse there might be a rat lurking under the seat in the lavvy at home.

It was nearly dinnertime when I remembered the eggs. In those days the hens roamed freely in the yard: that was before thieves came to steal any animals or birds they could find.

All the same I did wish that the hens were fenced in, because they laid their eggs anywhere. Jacques looked a bit astonished when I crawled under a bush and came out holding an egg. Soon he joined in the hunt, and eventually found three eggs under some bushes; then I found two in the hay in a corner.

When we went in for dinner Mam was delighted, "Six eggs, just what we need for tea."

We sat down to a delicious boiled dinner; all the meat and vegetables had been cooked in the saucepan. For 'afters' there was baked apples and custard.

Jacques ate and ate; he had seconds, and even thirds of the apples.

" He must be feeling happier," said Mum, "his appetite has come back."

I thought; perhaps his Grandmère doesn't know how much children eat.

"We'll be bringing the cows in for the winter in a few weeks, but they're in the top fields so we will go up to milk them," said Mam.

We set off; Jacques carried the bucket, I took the milking stool, and Mam took the big mallet. We walked through the lanes to the fields at the top of the cliffs.

"Not too close," called Mam, when Jacques went near the edge.

I walked over to him. Far below there was the surge of the sea, and the foam of the waves splashing the rocks, while gulls glided effortlessly overhead, then dived down, only to soar up again into the sky.

We went back to Mam, who was sitting on the wooden stool, her head on the cow's flank, and watched her hands pulling on the teats. The milk splashed into the bucket, making bubbles on the surface.

When the bucket was full we carried it between us, then carefully poured the milk, with 'a swoosh', into the big metal churns that Papa had left in a corner of the field.

I knew the names of all the cows and pointed out my favourites, Buttercup, Star and Daisy. When the milking was finished the cows were untethered. Jacques held onto Daisy's rope, I held Star and Buttercup, and Mam led the rest, as we took them to the trough to drink.

It was a good thing that it wasn't hot, because cows really suffered in summer when they were unable to move into the cool shade. Everyone knew that cattle could not be allowed to wander because the fields are too small, and they would destroy the grass. All the same, it wasn't much fun being a cow.

After the cows had been watered we led them to new patches of grass. Mam rolled up her sleeves, lifted the mallet, and puffing and panting drove each stake into the earth. Just as the last stake was being driven in Papa drove Punch into the field to collect the churns.

He puffed and sweated, as he hoisted them onto the cart.

When the last churn was in place we all climbed up. Jacques sat next to Papa, and was allowed to hold the reins, while I shouted 'gee up' and clicked my tongue. It was exciting being so high up, and looking over tall hedges and walls into nearby fields, and gardens.

When Punch started to trot Jacques laughed, and it was good to know he was so happy.

We had boiled eggs, bread and jam and cream for tea, then it was time to go home.

The journey back was much easier; we seemed to whizz down the hills. By the time we reached the front gate it was time for bed. Before he went in Jacques picked up Tibby Puss, and stroked him. I think Tibs reminded him of home.

SCHOOL
Chapter 5

It wasn't long before Jacques started school. He went to the parish school of St. Martin's. I went to the Convent at the top of my lane. If they'd taken boys Jacques might have liked it, because he was a Catholic, and the nuns came from France and spoke French.

Grandmamma paid all my fees, and kept saying, "It's very expensive. You must work hard, and be a credit to the family."

That proved to be difficult, because there came the time when I was always in trouble.

At first it was exciting, especially when Grandmamma took me to Town to buy my uniform; I'd never before had so many new clothes. The only problem was that everything was at least two sizes too big.

"We must leave room for growth," she kept repeating.

The uniform was very posh; there were even two hats, a summer panama, and black winter velour, and badges to put onto the hats and blazer. We didn't realise then that soon the shops would be empty, and there would only be clothes and shoes that were second, or third hand.

On the first day of school we walked down the long drive, and turned a corner. There was the convent, made of granite. Next to it the tall white building, which Dad said looked like a factory.

"That's the school," Mum said, "it's very big because there are so many classrooms, and dormitories where the boarders sleep."

There were girls milling about, some as big as grown ups. I felt a bit apprehensive, and wasn't sure that I wanted to go to school.

We went to a door at the side, to the kindergarten.

A nun came out, "You must be Marianne Renouf. I am Madam De La Rosa. Say good-bye to your Mother and come with me."

She held out her hand and in we went.

I'd never seen a nun close up, so had a good look. She wore cream, soft woollen robes down to the ground, with an embroidered heart on the front, and a bonnet with a ruff around her face. Behind the ruff was a long piece of material that went down her back.

The classroom was warm and sunny, and girls were sitting on chairs at little tables.

Madam De La Rosa said, "This is Marianne Renouf, she can sit at the same desk as you Iris."

Iris had black hair, dark brown eyes and a big smile.

At play time the bell rang, and we all went to the cloakroom. There was a row of doors; we had to take turns going in. Inside was a little lavvy, just the right size for me, it even had a flush to pull.

When we had finished Madam De La Rosa said, "If you need to go to the lavatory you must always put up your hand and say, 'Please may I be excused?" I knew Grandmamma would approve of that.

I really liked school, and soon Iris and I had another friend, Jane, and the three of us became inseparable.

By the time Jacques arrived I'd moved to a new class. We both had to work hard at school so were pleased when it was half term.

On the first day of the holiday I woke up very early, it was still dark, but Mum and Dad were moving about outside. Of course, it was Monday, washday. There was splashing and clanking, as they filled the copper with water from the well, and lit the fire under the copper to heat the water.

After breakfast Jacques arrived. We went out to the yard, which was covered with a tin roof in case of rain, where all the washing was done.

The sky was blue, the sun was shining but the wind was blowing, and it felt very cold. The water in the copper was bubbling.

"Don't come too near," warned Mum, as she lifted in the sheets and towels that had been soaking overnight, and dropped them into the copper.

There was the smell and sound of the boiling clothes; the white frothy bubbles cascading over the top, and splashing down the side onto the ground.

We both stood well back as Mum took out the boiling clothes, and put them in baths of water to rinse.

Our task was turning the enormous handle that turned the wooden rollers of the mangle. We watched as the water was squeezed out, and splashed on the ground as Mum guided through the folded sheets.

We had to work with all our might.

"Cor," said Jacques, " this is hard work."

We put the clothes into the basket, and carried it to the top of the garden. Thank goodness it's windy and dry, I thought, otherwise everything would be dried on the lines in the kitchen, and that was horrid, all clammy and muggy.

While Mum hung out the things we took turns on the swing. As the sheets billowed out the swing soared higher and higher. It was such a windy day the sheets were flapping, so it sounded as if we were on a sailing ship.

When all the clothes were pegged out we sat on the steps drinking glasses of milk, and eating home made biscuits, while Mum sipped her tea.

Then I had a good idea, "Let's blow bubbles."

We went indoors and Mum shaved soap off the big bar, and whisked it up in a bowl, and gave us two clay pipes. We went to the top of the steps, dipped the pipes in the soapy water and blew.

The bubbles were iridescent, and enormous. We gently shook the pipes and both bubbles rose into the air, changing shimmering colours, blue, gold, green, red, as they drifted higher and higher, until they flew over the hedge into the field.

We spent the rest of the morning having competitions, who could blow the biggest bubble, or whose bubble would fly highest.

It was such fun we were surprised when Mum called, "Dinner's ready."

We had the usual washday dinner, cold meat from the Sunday roast, boiled potatoes and pickles.

Mum said, "It's such a windy day the clothes will be ready to iron after we've finished eating."

"It is windy," agreed Dad, "let's make kites."

Jacques looked puzzled. "Kites fly," I tried to explain, "soon you'll see what I mean."

When the dishes were cleared away Dad went to the shed. He came back with some strips of wood, which he hammered into two kite shapes, with cross pieces in the middle.

Suddenly Jacques shouted with excitement, "Cerf–volant, cerf-volant."

Dad nodded, "That must be kite in French. Now Marianne please get some rags and string."

When I came back he had sheets of brightly coloured tissue paper that he used to pack tomatoes to send to England.

First we had to tear the rags into short strips, and Dad tied them on two pieces of string, "These will be the tails," he explained. Then he tied a ball of string onto each kite.

Next he mixed flour with water, to make cold water paste.

"Now," he said, "You must paste the paper onto the frames. Then leave them to dry, so they can fly."

We set to work; my kite was blue and yellow, and Jacques's red and green. When we'd finished we wandered into the living room, and watched Mum ironing.

She had two heavy irons; one was getting hot on the stand on the fire, and she ironed a sheet with the other.

"Time to change the irons over," she said, "this is too cool."

She picked up the other iron and spat on the base and it sizzled. "Just right," she said, and carried on ironing.

As the ironing finished Dad came back, "When we can afford it we'll buy an electric iron."

Mum smiled with anticipation, then she said, "There's a gale, the kites should fly well."

We took our kites; the paper was firmly stuck on, and went up to the field. Jacques had obviously flown a kite before; he ran into the wind, the kite trailing behind. Suddenly it started to fly, soaring higher and higher.

I'd never flown a kite, and needed help. It took three goes, and then up it went. I held firmly to the ball of string, as the kite tugged it felt as if it wanted to escape. I let the string out slowly, and soon the two kites were dancing overhead, the tails of rags trailing behind.

We flew the kites until it was dusk and time to go home, and decided to fly them again the next day, but when I woke up in the morning there wasn't a breath of wind.

"Never mind," said Dad, "You and Jacques can play in the vinery."

The vinery belonged to Grandmamma and Grandpa, and Dad worked there in the daytime. Sometimes at night, and at the weekends, he worked for the St John's Ambulance Brigade, helping people who were injured, and taking people to hospital.

The vinery was just a little way up the lane, and after breakfast we walked there.

"Where are the grapes?" Jacques asked.

Dad looked puzzled, then he laughed. "We only have two vines, but long ago we did grow grapes, that's why it's called a vinery, but now we grow tomatoes."

Jacques nodded that he understood.

Then we explored. First into the packing shed where tomatoes were put into chip baskets, with P. A. Renouf on them, and sent to England.

We passed the deep pit, which held the boiler that was used to heat the greenhouses. Then the windmill, which clanked and rattled, whenever the wind blew, and pumped up the water from the deep, deep well to the greenhouses.

At last we came to the big field, and went to the large clump of bamboo. We pushed our way in and came to a little clearing, right in the middle, and looked around.

The rays of the sunlight slanted through the leaves, which rustled in the breeze. The ground was covered in old bamboo leaves, and when we sat down it was soft and comfortable.

"Let's make a camp," I suggested.

"Yes!" Jacques shouted.

The rest of the week was spent at the camp. Soon we had collected old dishes, knives, forks, and spoons. Mum gave us two biscuit tins, one for paper and crayons, the other for biscuits and sweets.

On the last day of the holiday we spent the whole day there, and had a picnic of sandwiches and apples.

When we'd finished eating Jacques sighed, "Tomorrow we go to school, then no camp."

I nodded sadly, then cheered up, "Never mind, soon it'll be my birthday, and then Christmas."

"Yes," said Jacques, "and anyway, this is the best camp on the whole island."

But we didn't know then what we were going to discover, much later, in the wilderness.

Marianne, a year before the war began.

THE FIRST CHRISTMAS
Chapter 6

"**D**o you know," said Dad to Grandpa, "Jacques has been in Guernsey for three months, and there hasn't been any fighting in France, the only fighting has been far away in Poland."

Grandpa looked thoughtful, "He could have stayed at home. I don't think the Germans will ever get into France, the Maiginot Line will keep them out, but his parents will be happier knowing he's totally safe in Guernsey."

What's the Maginot Line?" I asked.

Grandpa spoke decisively, "It's a long, long line of defences that has been built along the border of France, which the Germans will never get through."

Good, I thought, perhaps now people will stop talking about war. All I could think about was my birthday, which was nearly here.

When I came downstairs on my birthday morning, to my horror, there wasn't a present in sight.

Mum smiled, "Happy birthday! You're going to have one big present from every one this year, and we're going to town to try it for size."

Not clothes, it was really awful having clothes as presents. Well, that's what I thought then, it was different later.

After breakfast we hurried to town, and went straight to Uncle Bill Green's cycle shop. Inside was a red bicycle, with a bell, a carrier, and a saddlebag at the back.

I sat on the saddle, the bike was just the right size, and I rang the bell, and the sound echoed around the shop.

Uncle Bill laughed, "You obviously like your present, I'll drop it off when I come home for dinner."

We'd finished eating when he arrived; the bike was even smarter than I remembered. We went out into the lane. Dad held the saddle while I pedalled. He let go, at first the bike wobbled, then I was cycling by myself.

"Don't forget the brakes," Dad shouted, as the cycle increased speed down a little hill, but I managed to stop without falling off.

Jacques was standing by the gate watching, "Please teach him how to ride," I pleaded. So Dad set off again, and before long Jacques could ride.

Everyday after school we took turns riding up and down, but it was cold waiting for a turn.

"If only you had a bike we could go exploring," I said shivering.

Jacques shook his head, "There's no money, Grandmère says we must count every penny, she says I eat and eat, and that costs a lot."

"Come and see what I have hidden in the shed in the vinery," Dad said one morning when he came home from the Ambulance Station.

We walked into the shed. There was a boy's bike, just the same size as mine, but it was very battered; the wheels were bent and the tyres worn out.

Dad looked proud, "It belonged to the son of a man I work with, it's too small for him now, so we'll give it to Jacques for Christmas."

I felt doubtful, "It's all broken, he'll never be able to ride it."

"Wait and see," said Dad, "I'm taking it to Uncle Bill's shop to find out what he can do, then I'm going to paint it."

When the bike came back all the bent bits, and the spokes were straight, there was a new saddle and new tyres. Dad went to the vinery every spare minute, and was busy painting. I emptied my moneybox, and bought a shiny bell, which Dad took away to put on the bike.

Soon we were busy preparing for Christmas. One wet afternoon Jacques and I had masses of brightly coloured paper strips, which we made into loops, and linked together until we were surrounded by piles of paper chains.

When Mum came in, she laughed, "You seem to be sitting in the middle of a rainbow."

The next day Dad went to Westwood to cut holly from a bush in the garden. He was just carrying it into the house when there was the clip -clop of Punch's hooves as he stopped at the front gate.

Papa and Mam Camp climbed down from the trap, and came inside. Papa was carrying a bunch of mistletoe that had grown on an apple tree in the orchard. Mam was holding a big chicken for our Christmas dinner.

We sat in the kitchen, and drank tea, and ate sandwiches and cake. Everyone talked about what they were going to do in the holiday.

Then Papa said, "We must get back to the farm before it gets dark. Would you like a ride to the top of the lane?"

"Yes please," Jacques and I said at the same time. We ran out, and climbed on the seat between Mam and Papa.

Punch started to trot, "He knows he's going home," said Jacques.

We were sorry when we had to get off, but stood and waved, and shouted 'Happy Christmas,' until the trap disappeared around the corner.

The next day we set to work decorating the house. The paper chains were hung up. Mum stuck little blobs of cotton wool onto the wooden beams and it looked just like snow. There was holly behind the pictures, and a big vase full of holly on top of the piano. In the hall the bunch of mistletoe was hanging from the lampshade.

When it was all finished Dad went outside and brought in the little Christmas tree, which he had dug up from the garden, and put into a bucket. Jacques and I decorated the branches with a star, a glass ball, a glass Father Christmas, a bell, a snowman, and four chocolate shapes covered in bright shiny paper.

At the top of the tree Mum placed the fairy that she'd made. We covered the bucket with red crepe paper, and put some tinsel on the branches.

"It's perfect," I was saying when Dad walked in with a box; and we watched as he lifted off the lid.

"Now we have electricity we can have fairy lights," he said, and we saw coloured bulbs.

We helped to put the lights on the tree, then the light was switched off, and the fairy lights switched on. They shone brightly in the darkness.

We gasped in astonishment, the lights were so beautiful.

Jacques went home, and Mum and Dad went to get tea. I sat with the electric light off, and looked at the lights, the cards, the paper chains, the holly and the Christmas tree.

I took a deep breath, Christmas! The scent of resin from the tree made my nose twitch, and I took a deep breath, and thought; even if I couldn't see, I would know that it's Christmas. There was the smell of mince pies cooking in the kitchen, best of all the smell of oranges and tangerines, which we only had at Christmas time.

On Christmas morning I woke up very early, there was something by my feet, it was my stocking! I carried it carefully, and climbed into Mum and Dad's bed and took out my presents.

There was a little doll, with a set of day and night clothes, a painting book and a box of paints, a book of fairy stories, a sugar mouse with string for the tail, a tangerine and some nuts.

It was a lovely stocking, but I said "I'll play with everything later. When can we give Jacques the bike?"

"As soon as we've eaten breakfast, and before our visitors arrive," replied Dad.

When the table was cleared we went out to the shed. There was the bike, the green paint glinting and shining, as good as new.

I wheeled it carefully next door, and knocked. There was the sound of bolts being drawn back, and out looked Grandmère and Jacques.

His mouth opened in astonishment, then he shouted, "Une bicylette, une bicyclette."

I pushed the bike forward; "It's for you, for Christmas."

He stared at the bike, and then he looked at Mum and Dad, "Oh merci beaucoup, I mean, thank you, thank you, a bike of my very own!"

Jacques rang the bell; it was extremely loud.

"I bought that for you," I told him.

He grinned, "It's good, thank you very much."

There was no time to play because Grandmamma and Grandpa were walking through the gate, Grandpa calling out, "Merry Christmas, Merry Christmas."

While dinner was cooking we opened the presents from under the tree. Mum had scent, and a book of crosswords. Dad had some hankies, and cigarettes. Grandmamma had talcum powder, and hankies. Grandpa had shaving soap, and tobacco, Grandmamma frowned when she saw that, but he smiled with delight.

I had a miniature tea set to go in the dolls' house, and a book called 'Heidi,' with beautiful pictures.

"Now," I said, "I'm going to get your presents," and came back with four little parcels. Inside Mum's and Grandmamma's was a little mouse. Dad and Grandpa each had a tortoise. They were all made from shells that I'd collected on the beach.

"Now I know why you wanted a tube of real glue," said Mum. Everyone agreed that they were perfect presents.

Soon dinner was ready. There was roast chicken, stuffing, roast potatoes, roast parsnips and Brussels sprouts."

"I wish we could have chicken every week, instead of only at Christmas," I said.

"Don't be so greedy," scolded Grandmamma.

But Mum said, "That would be lovely, but it's much too expensive."

Next we had Christmas pudding and white sauce, which I didn't really like, but ate it up because I hoped to find the lucky silver sixpence, and sure enough I did.

After we'd finished eating we washed up, and then everyone said that they were going to have a snooze, except me.

I had put on my coat and pixie hood, and ran next door. Jacques came out and we got our bikes, we puffed up the hill, and then whizzed down ringing our bells loudly.

When Dad called us in tea was on the table, and Grandmère came in and joined us. It was a real party tea, we even had crackers. There was ham and pickles, mince pies, trifle, red jelly, and a big Christmas cake that Grandmamma had made. On the top was a Christmas tree, and a little hill made of icing with children sliding down on a sledge. All around the cake were little silver balls you could eat.

When we'd finished eating Dad cut two little parcels off the Christmas tree. Inside mine was a celluloid doll, and Jacques had a tin engine. Next we each had another parcel, and inside there were balloons to blow up, and last of all we each had a chocolate Father Christmas.

Now all the parcels had been opened Mum got up and put out the electric light. We sat in the firelight, while the fairy lights twinkled and shone, and ate dates and tangerines, while Dad cracked nuts for us all.

We sang carols, then songs that made Jacques and me laugh. Dad said they were Music Hall songs. Some of them made Grandmamma frown, because they were rather rude, and that made us laugh even more.

I was late going to bed, but couldn't get to sleep, and kept thinking about the wonderful day. Best of all, no one had mentioned the war, not even once.

The fairy doll Marianne's mother made for the Christmas tree.

WAITING
Chapter 7

The days after Christmas were dark and gloomy, every one seemed scared and they talked continuously about war. The wireless set was on all the time.

"The Germans are coming nearer, Belgium has surrendered," Grandpa said.

"Why didn't the Maginot Line stop them?" I asked.

"Because they went around it," he replied scornfully. It sounded as if he thought they'd cheated.

Dad said, "The Dutch will stop them, because they've broken the dykes and flooded the land."

But that didn't work, and the Germans stormed across, and there was fighting in France.

"I hope Ma Mère and Mon Père are safe," Jacques said. "Grandmère says that they are, but perhaps she's wrong, and they're hurt."

"I bet they're not," I said, and he cheered up a bit.

When Grandmamma and Grandpa thought I wasn't listening, they whispered about terrible things that had happened to people and children in the Great War.

That night, and every night afterwards, I had nightmares. Men wearing helmets, and sometimes gas masks, and always carrying guns, were chasing me, and there were rats scurrying about.

I would wake up, my heart thumping, feeling hot and sweaty, and creep into Mum and Dad's bed and cuddle up. But even there, I sometimes, had horrible dreams.

I asked Jacques if he had nightmares. He shook his head, but perhaps what he thought in the daytime was worse than any dream.

One morning Dad came home looking worried.

"I was going past the harbour, and saw a little, old, battered fishing boat mooring on the quay side. There was the skipper, and some women and children. The boat was so full she was almost sinking.

The people looked terrified and exhausted. They had little bundles that held their possessions. They told me that the Germans were getting nearer and nearer to the coast. The enemy must be very near if people risked their lives trying to escape."

"The Germans won't come here, will they?" I asked.

"No," he said reassuringly, " The British government has said that the islands are a safe place to stay during the war. We're too small for Hitler to bother about. Anyway we govern ourselves so we won't allow them to come."

But he was wrong.

The next day I went into the living room, Mum and Dad were reading the paper, and they looked scared.

Pushing between them I read:

[GUERNSEY PRESS 19 JUNE 1940]
Evacuation of: 1. Children of school age and   2. Children of under school age to take place tomorrow. Mothers of under school age may accompany their children.   All persons wishing to evacuate to report to the Parish Constables.

"What does it mean? What does that mean?" I asked, feeling frightened because Mum and Dad looked so worried.

"It means," said Dad,"that the Germans are coming, and children are going to be evacuated to England."

"What's evacuated?"

Dad frowned, "Children are going to be taken away to a safe place in England."

"Would we go on a boat?" That sounded exciting.

Mum said, "Not we, you. We couldn't come with you; you would have to go with the nuns from the Convent.

That was terrible news, I didn't want to go.

From that moment everything was confusing. Dad didn't go to work; we had to make up our minds what to do for the best.

There were lots of arguments.

"Marianne won't go with the school." Mum said decisively, "maybe, later on, they will let anyone who wants to escape leave, and then we can all go."

Grandpa didn't agree, he said, "I think she should go with the school, if the Germans come here everyone is in great danger."

Mum suddenly interrupted, "I know terrible things happen in war, and terrible things may happen here, but she is too young to be sent away by herself. Submarines might sink the boat, or aeroplanes bomb it; she'll stay here with us."

Everyone was trying to make up their minds. Aunt Elsie left with her baby, but she left her Scottie dog behind. Then all my cousins left, and most of the children on the island went too.

I asked Jacques if he was going.

He shook his head, "I feel safe with my Grandmère."

Poor Jacques, I thought, he might as well have stayed with his Mum and Dad in France.

When we went to Westwood I said, "Nearly all the children in the lane have gone, and do you know Adele, from opposite, has been crying and crying?"

"Why should she cry?" questioned Grandmamma.

Mum explained, "She's sad and frightened because her boyfriend has left, like so many other young men, to join the army and fight."

Grandmamma huffed, and said, "If she survives it won't be long before she gets a new man, she has boyfriends like we have hot dinners. That girl is a common hussy."

I often thought that Grandmamma was really unkind.

Mum began to get frightened when so many people left and said, "If we have the chance I'll take Marianne to England," and she packed a little bag.

When I told Jacques we were going to leave he didn't say anything, just shrugged his shoulders, and looked sad.

The next morning Dad came in looking very serious, and said, "It's too late to do anything, the last boat has gone."

I rushed out, and called to Jacques, "It's all right, we're not going, we've left it too late."

Jacques gave a big grin and said, "Tres bien! I mean jolly good," and I felt happier than any day since the news about the evacuation.

The next day seemed very peaceful, but we were only allowed to play indoors, or close to the back door because there were German planes flying high overhead.

We were playing marbles when I whispered, so Mum wouldn't hear, "What do you think Germans are like?"

Jacques looked serious, "They are cruel, they have guns and daggers, and they kill people."

I nodded, "That's what Grandpa says. I think they wear helmets, and have angry faces like monsters, and they don't like children."

Just then Mum called us in for our elevenses. I hoped and hoped that the soldiers wouldn't come, and everything would be all right again.

That June evening it was beautifully warm and sunny, and Mum decided that we would go to the Convent dairy, as usual, to buy our milk.

I liked going to the dairy, the Nuns who worked on the farm wore black robes, and were called Soeur, which means sister in French. Sometimes they gave me a sweet.

The dairy was at the bottom of a small hill, a little distance from the Convent. We were just going through the gate, and along the farm track when there was the sound of many planes. As the sound grew louder Mum took tight hold of our hands, and we ran into the dairy.

No sooner were we inside the door than there was the roar of explosions, and the building seemed to shake. There were three sisters, all of them praying. Mum held us both tight, and Soeur Angelique put her hand on my head, and prayed even more fervently.

The noise of the bombs was louder than the loudest thunderstorm. When there was a lull in the bombardment the prayers of the sisters seemed to echo all around.

When the bombing ceased, and the sound of the planes receded into the distance, we hurried home, and saw Dad running towards us.

"Thank God you're safe. I was certain they'd think the school was a factory, and it would be bombed."

When we reached home it looked exactly the same as when we left. There was no damage, the sun was still shining; it was the same warm peaceful evening.

Suddenly Grandmère ran out and clutched Jacques, "Mon Dieu, Mon Dieu, you are safe."

She was crying, and kissing him at the same time. Jacques looked very embarrassed.

We said goodnight to Jacques and Mrs. Le Marquand, and went indoors for supper. Mum and Dad didn't eat anything, just drank cups of tea, but I ate strawberry jam sandwiches, and drank a glass of milk.

I'd just finished eating when the front door opened, and Uncle Bill from the cycle shop came in.

"Terrible things have happened," he said. "People have been killed, and many injured at the harbour. All the glass in the windows in town has been blown out, but no buildings destroyed."

Later, lying in bed, there was the sound of Mum and Dad's anxious voices talking late into the night, their voices a background murmur to my sleep.

Despite our disturbed night we were all up as early as usual to get Dad's breakfast, in time for him to get to work by half past seven. I gave him a kiss and waved good-bye from the gate.

Mum and I were just sitting down to eat our breakfast when we heard the sound of Dad's bike coming back up the path. He flung open the door, and shut it quickly behind him. He was puffing, and was very pale.

He sat in a chair and said, "There is a German at the cross roads, and he's holding a gun."

TO THE PEOPLE OF GUERNSEY

IN THESE GRAVE AND ANXIOUS TIMES, I STRONGLY EXHORT ONE AND ALL TO REMAIN CALM AND AVOID PANIC. IT BEHOVES US TO BEHAVE AS TRUE AND LOYAL MEN AND WOMEN OF GUERNSEY AND TO APPLY OURSELVES TO OUR DUTIES WITH THAT QUIET DETERMINATION WHICH HAS ALWAYS CHARACTERISED ALL ISLANDERS. I, THEREFORE, IMPLORE YOU NOT TO BE ALARMED BY REASON OF THE PRECAUTIONARY STEPS WHICH THE AUTHORITIES ARE TAKING.

LET US REMEMBER THAT EVACUATION IS VOLUNTARY. THERE IS NO COMPULSION.

BEYOND TEACHERS, CHILDREN OF SCHOOL AGE AND UNDER WITH MOTHERS OR OTHER RELATIONS IN CHARGE, AS WELL AS MEN OF MILITARY AGE, IT IS IMPRACTICABLE FOR OTHERS TO HOPE TO BE EVACUATED.

VICTOR G. CAREY

JUNE 20, 1940.
LIEUTENANT-GOVERNOR AND BAILIFF.

Top: A message from the Bailiff endeavouring to calm the panic stricken population. Below: Bombed lorries at the harbour.

A DIFFERENT WORLD
Chapter 8

I couldn't really believe that there were soldiers with guns on our island; perhaps at any moment they might come running down the lane, break down our doors and attack us.

Mum must have had the same thought because she looked scared.

"I'm sure that everything will be all right," Dad said reassuringly, "let's telephone Westwood, and see what they're doing."

Grandpa told us that some Germans had walked past, so they'd bolted the doors, and we should do the same.

Then Mum telephoned the farm. Mam said they hadn't seen sight nor sign of any Germans, and were busy as usual looking after the animals.

We'd just finished dinner when there was a thump on the mat; the Press had arrived. We all crowded around and read-----

'By Order Of The Commandant Of The German Forces In The Occupation Of The Island Of Guernsey.'
'We will respect the population in Guernsey but should anyone attempt to cause the least trouble serious measures will be taken and the town will be bombed.'

Dad read out a list of orders, "They don't really apply to us, people can't use their cars, or buy petrol, well we haven't got a car. We haven't any weapons to hand in, and I'm nor a member of the armed services, so I don't have to give myself up. The only thing that matters is the curfew. That means that we can't go out between ten o'clock at night and seven in the morning."

"What happens if we do?" I asked.

"It would be very serious, we'd be severely punished, and if we didn't stop they might even shoot us."

I often used to go out early, before Mum and Dad were dressed, and had no idea of the time. I thought that it would be a good idea to check in future.

Suddenly Dad said, "The paper boy had no problems delivering the paper, I think it will be safe to go out."

We were walking down the front path when there was knocking from the upstairs window next door. I looked up and saw Jacques.

He leaned out and called, "Where are you going?"

"To Westwood."

He looked mournful, "I have to stay in. All our doors are locked and bolted, Grandmère says we are in great danger."

Suddenly we saw Grandmère standing behind him. She didn't say hello, she just pulled him back inside, and shut the window.

"Why's she so scared?" I asked.

"I guess she's remembering the Great War, and is frightened; but that happened long ago, we don't need to worry," said Dad.

We started walking to Westwood and came to the crossroads.

Dad pointed, "That's where the soldier was standing, I wonder where he's gone."

When we arrived at Westwood they were astonished to see us.

"What a risk you took, you should have stayed at home," scolded Grandpa.

"There wasn't any danger," said Dad bravely.

Grandmamma interrupted, "Sheer stupidity. Anyway it be won't be long before they show their true colours, then you'll see the danger we're in."

Before we went back home Grandpa took me into the drawing room looking very serious.

"I want you to listen carefully to what I'm telling you. These are very dangerous times. If they give an order such as "Halt," do what they say immediately, or you put your life at risk. You must always remember that they are the enemy."

"Well, they've arrived," Mum said as we walked home, "and nothing awful has happened. Perhaps we'll be all right."

I thought about what Grandmamma and Grandpa had said, and wasn't too sure.

After a couple of days Grandmère let Jacques out to play, and by Saturday she even let him come to Town with us.

As we walked through the streets there were flags flying, each one red, with a black shape.

Jacques pointed, "They're called Swastikas, that's what the Nazis, who follow Hitler, put on badges."

There were lots of enemy soldiers walking on the pavements. When they passed I looked down at the ground, it was really silly, but I thought that if I didn't look at them they couldn't see me.

As we walked up the High Street who should we bump into but Grandmamma, who looked extremely angry.

"Do you know I came to Town to buy some food, and the shops are almost empty," she grumbled, "The Germans are swaggering around as if they own this island. They've been buying expensive things and sending them home to Germany.

Guernsey people are as bad; they're buying all the food, and hoarding it, even though that's forbidden. I hope they're caught."

Mum sighed and looked worried, "They say we'll be living under siege conditions soon, and won't be able to get food, but I've only enough money to buy what we need this week."

Suddenly there was the sound of music coming nearer and nearer, around the corner marched a military band. Everyone stood still. The soldiers were smart; the sun glinted on the instruments. The music grew louder as the band passed.

I couldn't stop smiling, and longed to march and dance. Jacques was tapping his feet.

Grandmamma said, "Stand still, and behave," and as there was no option that's what we did.

Soon we became used to seeing German soldiers walking along the roads and driving cars and trucks. Ordinary people weren't allowed to drive, so there wasn't much traffic, and we were allowed out on our bikes.

What was really strange was that there weren't many children, and lots of houses were empty, the people who once lived in them had gone to England. We peeped in through the windows of one empty house. There was still food on the table, and clothes and toys scattered on the floor.

"Gosh," Jacques said, "they must have left in a hurry."

It wasn't long before school started again. Going back was peculiar, there were hardly any children walking up the drive, but inside there was the same smell of polish, chalk and wax crayons.

Now there were only six children left in my class. I was really pleased to see my special friends Iris and Jane; I had worried that they might have been evacuated with everyone else.

We waited, suddenly the door opened. We all quickly jumped up, curtsied and chorused, "Good morning Reverend Mother."

She looked at us and said, "Good morning children. I am pleased to see you. As you know most of the nuns and sisters have left the Convent, and are now in England. You are very fortunate that Madam Marie Helene is here, and will teach you. I expect you to work hard, and will be interested in your progress."

As she swept out of the room we stared at Madam Marie Helene, who used to teach another class. She was dressed, like all the teaching nuns, with the embroidered heart on her gown, and before we knew it we were working harder than we'd ever worked before.

Although there weren't many children there were still lots of rules. We all had to wear tabliers, which were black overalls, with sleeves down to the wrist, and on warm days they were always too hot. We aren't allowed to run in the corridors, and had to be silent as we moved around the school. We had to curtsey, both indoors and out, when meeting Reverend Mother.

Even with all the rules I liked going to school. Madam Marie Helene was a good teacher, she was pleased with our work, and was a really good storyteller. Best of all it was always peaceful in her class, we never had to think about the war, and about not having enough to eat.

When I came home one afternoon Jacques was waiting for me, "You won't believe it, the Germans have taken over St Martin's School, and we're in a big house in the Vallon. We can see the sea in the distance, but the worst thing is we haven't got a football field."

One day he came back and said excitedly, "A German officer rode past my school on a magnificent horse. We all crowded to the gate and he stopped. The teachers were really mean they called us back into school."

The German officer passed the school every day and Jacques talked and talked about the horse.

One day, when he came back, I could tell he was bursting with excitement.

"Come up the garden with me," he said. As soon as we were far away from the house he whispered, "You'll never guess. The German officer was late today, and I met him on the way home.

He stopped the horse and I went near, and asked, 'what's he called?' He said, 'Bucephelus.' Do you think that one day he might let me ride him?"

I was horrified, "Jacques, if Grandmère finds out you've talked to a German she'll be furious. You know it's dangerous."

"I'm not sure, he seemed all right, and Bucephelus is wonderful.

Do you remember the soldiers in the band, they didn't look fierce and they were so smart."

I nodded in agreement, "I thought they'd look like monsters, but they didn't, and I'm sure the soldier banging a drum winked at me. Yet the grown ups are all scared of the Germans, but perhaps we don't need to be afraid."

It wasn't long before we changed our minds because the soldiers we saw next did look frightening.

We were in town with Mam Camp, who'd taken eggs to the market to sell. We were by the harbour, passing the Town Church, when there was the sound of marching feet.

A long column of soldiers, in rows, marched past. They were wearing helmets, greeny-grey uniforms, and long shiny black boots. They all had guns against their shoulders. There was only the sound of the tramp, tramp, tramp of their feet, and the shouted orders.

They were staring straight ahead. It was impossible to imagine them ever smiling, and a shiver ran down my spine. These were like the men in my dreams, the men Grandpa had warned me about.

Jacques must have had the same feeling. He was quiet for ages, then whispered, "I wonder what has happened to my mother and father?"

The German band seen by the children.

THE SECRET GARDEN
Chapter 9

We decided to keep well away from any Germans we met, and everything was fine until one of the very worst things in the Occupation happened.

One evening the Press arrived and I read a notice, it said:

IT IS FORBIDDEN TO VISIT THE WHOLE SOUTH COAST, THESE LOCALITIES ARE EXTREMELY DANGEROUS.

THE COMMANDANT.

"Why's it dangerous?" I asked.

"The Germans are putting down mines," explained Dad, "to prevent the English soldiers landing. It means that we can't go down to our beach any more."

Not go to our beach, Moulin Huet? Jacques and I couldn't believe it. What were we going to do;? We usually went down every day. No picnics, no swimming, no rock climbing. It was unbelievable.

When Dad came back after driving the ambulance he would tell us about the signs that were going up around the cliffs. The first one he saw said, 'Achtung Minen', which meant,' beware of mines.'

The one we were interested in said', 'HALT, MINENGE FAHR,' and a picture of a skull and cross bones, like a pirate flag. He said that meant 'Stop, Stop mine field,' and the skull and cross bones meant death.

Sometimes there would be an explosion.

Dad would say, "That sounds like a mine."

I worried that someone might have been killed. Dad said that there had been a few accidents, but most often animals set off the mines.

"What animals?" I asked.

"Usually rabbits, but possibly dogs and cats.

That's when the worry about Tibby Puss began.

One lovely sunny day, in the holidays, we were in the lane and Jacques grumbled, "It's no fun not being able to go to the beach."

We'd stopped walking and were leaning on the gate of one of the houses where everyone had evacuated. Suddenly the gate swung open, and we fell over into the garden.

I quickly shut the tall gate.

"What are you doing?" Jacques asked.

"Well, we know no one lives here now, the hedge is so tall no one can see us, it's the perfect place to play."

Even though we were almost sure that there was no one in the house we crept around, moving quietly from bush to bush. There must have been children living there once, because there was a swing and a rope ladder hanging from a tree.

For the next few days we kept going back to the garden, but didn't go near the house, just in case someone was still there. At last we plucked up courage and cautiously tiptoed right up, and peered through the windows. The rooms were full of furniture, but there wasn't sight nor sound of anyone.

We tried to open the doors and windows, but they were all firmly locked.

"That's all right, it might be scary to go inside," I said, "anyway this is our secret garden, and we can come here whenever we want."

It was a lovely garden, full of flowers, but everything was over grown, and the grass on the lawn reached up to our waists. There was even a summerhouse, where we went on rainy days.

There was all kinds of fruit growing in the garden, and we ate strawberries, raspberries and gooseberries.

This was turning out to be a wonderful holiday, until the day when we were playing in the sunshine near the front of the house. I looked up at the white clouds high in the sky, and was enjoying the warmth of the sun on my face. It all seemed so peaceful, as if there couldn't be any fighting anywhere in the world.

I was looking at the pinky red tiles on the roof, and the sunlight shining on the windows. Suddenly I saw that there was someone looking out of a bedroom window. It was a man, my heart started to thump, it couldn't be, it was, a German soldier was staring straight at me.

In shock I stared back, then Jacques also looked up, gasped, grabbed my hand, and we ran out of the gate, down the lane into the cottage, slamming the door behind us.

After breakfast next day we went into the lane. The gate of our secret garden, and the front door, were open. Just then a lorry drove up, and four soldiers jumped out, and hurried inside.

Soon they reappeared carrying out furniture, and loaded it into the lorry then drove away. Before long they came back bringing different furniture, and lots of boxes.

Suddenly Jacques pulled me back behind the hedge, "Look out," he hissed, "there's the German we saw yesterday, he'll be mad at us for trespassing, p'raps he'll want us locked up."

The German stood looking around then went back inside. We hurried past the front gate, and walked further up the lane. To our astonishment there were more lorries, and more soldiers carrying furniture into the big house called Medecombra, so we knew Germans were coming to live in that house as well.

We spent the rest of the morning pretending to play in the stream, but really we were spying on all the activity.

I began to feel hungry; "We'd better go home, it must be time for dinner. I wonder what Mum's cooked. She read in the paper that this is a meatless week, she hasn't been to town to queue for fish, so it'll just be vegetables."

Jacques frowned, "We nearly always have vegetables, you're lucky, your Mum cooks lovely dinners."

We both hurried back home. When I went into the kitchen Mum was taking the earthenware pot out of the hay box, and there was the dusty, musty smell of the hay, which always made my nose twitch.

It was a long time ago when the hay box arrived; it was at the beginning of the Occupation. Dad and Papa had unloaded the big box off a cart, it looked like a blanket chest; but to my surprise they carried into the kitchen, and not upstairs.

Dad went out and returned with a sack of hay, and put it in the box. "What are you doing?" I asked.

Dad grinned, "This hay box will cook our food."

And sure enough it did. When food was boiling Mum put the saucepan inside, covered it with hay, put down the lid, and it carried on cooking slowly for hours.

We always had porridge for breakfast that had been cooking in the hay box all night. In winter, once the porridge was dished up, we'd sit around the table warming our hands on the bowls. I longed for sugar or golden syrup, but at least, as Mum said, porridge filled us up.

Today it was bean stew with lots of onions, best of all Mum had been able to get some salt from the black market, and so it was delicious.

When I was smaller I really thought that there would be a black stall in the market, but Grandpa told me it was a way of selling things for a lot of money, and this was forbidden, because all the food was supposed to be shared, and sold at a certain price. He said it was a way of making money by people who had hoarded food, and he hoped that the sellers would be caught.

Dad told me that he knew it was wrong to buy anything on the black market, but sometimes that was the only way we could get what we really needed, but never, ever, mention this at Westwood.

Just as we'd finished eating there was a knock at the door, and Jacques was waiting.

"Hang on a moment," said Mum, "can you take some apples to Grandmamma?"

I nodded as Mum gave me a basket.

"What did you have for dinner?" I asked as we walked up the lane.

"Boiled carrots and potatoes," Jacques replied, "and I'm still hungry."

I took two rosy eaters out of the basket, and we sat on the hedge, and ate every bit, even the cores. There was no sign of the trucks, and no sign of anyone in the house with the secret garden, which wasn't secret any more.

When we arrived at Westwood I told them about the Germans coming to live in the empty houses.

Grandpa looked very seriously at both of us and said, "I want you both to remember, keep way from the Germans, don't look at them or speak to them, they spell danger. Whatever you do never accept sweets or biscuits from them because they will almost certainly be poisoned."

He was still talking when there was the sound of traffic, and we all ran into the front garden. There were big lorries, and trucks full of soldiers passing.

To our astonishment a lorry, pulling an enormous gun, rumbled past. Then, in the distance, a discordant sound, which grew louder, and louder and louder, and around the corner came the strangest machines we'd ever seen. They were enormous. There were no wheels, only a continuous ridged track that moved slowly around and drove the machines forward.

The sound was terrifying, a terrible noise, there were squeaks, and creaks of metal that seemed to rattle and groan. The machines had black crosses painted on them; there was a big gun at the front, and a soldier, with a helmet on his head, standing inside looking out from the top of each machine. The machines made so much noise, and were so large I held Grandpa's hand tight.

As the sounds receded into the distance Jacques said, "Those are tanks, I've never seen them before."

Grandpa said, "That's right, they're made of strong metal, so strong that if the soldiers go inside, and close the thing called the turret, and there is shooting, they are safe. The gun is there to kill people, and destroy gun emplacements. The tanks are so big and strong they can knock down walls, trees, and even houses."

"What would happen if anyone fell under them?" I asked, "Would they be squashed, flat as flat, and killed?" He nodded in agreement.

As we were walking home Jacques said, "You're daft, you would hear a tank a mile off, no one would walk in front of a tank, they'd run away."

I felt a bit reassured, and just hoped that I could run fast enough.

We were walking down the lane, past the big house when the door opened, and a tall German, dressed in a black uniform strode past.

He didn't look at us, but Jacques stared, "Isn't his uniform smart, and just look at his cap, he must be a really important officer."

A few days later we were playing in the front garden when we were aware of someone standing by the hedge. It was German we'd seen at the window. He was smiling, he had a fat smiley face, and he beckoned.

There seemed no option other than to go to the hedge, so we walked across slowly. The soldier was holding a photograph of a small girl; she seemed to be about the same age as us. She has fair hair, just like me, I thought.

He said, "My girl," and a name we didn't know, it sounded like Freyda.

"Mr. Max." he said pointing at himself.

I pointed at myself and said, "Marianne," then pointed again and said, "Jacques."

Mr. Max put his hand in his pocket and took out four sweets, two were yellow and two were white, and held them out. We both said, "Thank you," and took two each.

Mr. Max gave us a wave, and walked away around the corner. Quickly we looked around, no one had seen us. We hid in the bushes, and tried to decide what to do.

I said, " Grandpa said never take sweets or biscuits from Germans, because they will be poisoned, but Mr. Max doesn't look as if he's a poisoner."

Jacques nodded, "Anyway he's got a little girl, so he must like children."

Slowly I unwrapped a white sweet, and had a lick, a little lick wouldn't hurt, and whispered "Lemon."

Jacques unwrapped a yellow sweet and licked, "Orange!"

We both smiled, and carried on licking. The sweets lasted for a whole week without any adults finding out.

When eventually they were finished, Jacques said, "Just imagine if we could have a sweet, every day."

"One a month would be enough for me," I said.

ORDER OF THE KOMMANDANT.

IT IS FORBIDDEN TO VISIT THE COAST SOUTHWARDS OF FORT GEORGE, THE WHOLE SOUTH COAST, THE COAST OF TORTEVAL TO THE IMPERIAL HOTEL, THE COAST OF THE PENINSULA FORT SAUMAREZ AND LIHOU ISLAND.

THESE LOCALITIES ARE EXTREMELY DANGEROUS.

THE KOMMANDANT.

4.2.1941. (4050

HALT 🕱 **HALT**

Minengefahr!

Beschädigung der Zäune und Betreten der Felder wegen Lebensgefahr bei Strafe verboten.

Above: The order that horrified the children.
Below: Warning of a mine field.

Above: A hay box used for cooking food.
Below: Tanks similar to those seen by the children.

CUP AND SAUCER.
Chapter 10

When we saw Mr Max he always smiled and waved, but he didn't give us any more sweets. "It's not fair," I grumbled, "I'm always hungry".

Mum sighed, "We're all hungry, the rations are so small we have to save everything we can."

Jacques and I had to help. There was hardly any coal so we collected wood and twigs that the wind has blown down, and stacked logs when Dad cut down old trees at the vinery.

We carried bucket after bucket of water from the well for the washing, and watched Mum trying to get clothes clean. It was really hard because there wasn't any soap, so she used washing soda that made her arms and hands raw red.

People always seemed to talk about the food they used to eat.

"They're daft," said Jacques, "the more you talk the hungrier you become, but I'd give anything for chocolate."

I shook my head, "Ice-cream for me, although I've almost forgotten what it tastes like."

"We're going to the farm today," Mum said one day at breakfast.

That was good news because we went there to get food to take home, even though this was strictly forbidden. Jacques knew our secret; the first time he came we hid eggs, milk, butter and cheese in our saddlebags.

"This is a bit scary," I said as we cycled home," if we're stopped and searched there will be terrible punishments."

Jacques frowned; "Well let's hope we don't get caught," and he started whistling to show the soldiers that we were just out for a ride.

I was pleased that Jacques was coming to the farm today, but hoped we wouldn't have to take Scotty for a walk. He was the dog my Aunty Elsie left when she took baby John David to England, just before the Germans came.

I wished she'd left the baby, and taken the dog. Scotty was bad tempered, growled and snapped. He used to be fat, but now he was thin, his coat was mangy; he was smelly and stubborn.

Mam was really anxious, she wanted him to survive to the end of the war, and be reunited with his owner. The trouble was that people were so hungry that pets were stolen and eaten. Mam wouldn't let Scotty out in the garden; he had to be taken for walks. When I was there I was the one to take him.

"You're a pest," I'd say as he either tugged at the lead, or refused to budge. The last time I'd been to the farm it was wet, and he kept stopping, it was irritating. I was so angry that I'd kept pulling him through puddles to teach him a lesson.

We came to an enormously deep puddle when he suddenly dashed forward, pulled me over and in I fell. My clothes were soaked, and I was muddy from head to foot, but didn't let go of the lead. I was sure that he did it on purpose.

When we got back Mam was furious, even though he hadn't got away, and I'd held tight.

"I don't understand it," she kept saying. "He hates water, you must have been teasing him."

What was even worse than the scolding was the bath in cold water to get rid of the mud. All my clothes had to be washed, and then I had to sit in a towel until they dried.

When Jacques heard about what had happened he couldn't stop laughing. In the end I had to laugh too, but there'd been nothing to laugh about at the time.

It was a lovely sunny day when we cycled into the farmyard, and there was no sign of Scotty. It seemed strange that life on the farm was always the same, when everything else was so different and dangerous. We couldn't see any soldiers with guns on their belts, no sound of marching feet, no flags with the black shapes blowing in the wind.

I took a deep breath, knowing why it was good to be here, it felt safe.

As we got off our bikes Mam came out of the back door. She was smiling, and walked over and gave us all a hug.

"Let's go down to the beach, it's a very low tide," she said. "We need to get carrageen moss seaweed, to dry to make blancmange, and we'll get winkles and limpets at the same time. We may as well take the shrimping nets."

I was so excited; but then noticed that Mum was frowning, and clenching her hands.

"We can't, it's much too dangerous," she protested.

"It's not a restricted area, there aren't any mines, and the fishermen go down quite safely," Mam said reassuringly.

We both begged to go, and in the end Mum reluctantly agreed.

Jacques and I skipped and ran down the lane, there was no sound of trucks. We stood still, it was so peaceful, there was the murmur of Mum's voice behind us, and the singing of birds in the hedge. I looked up and could see the green leaves fluttering against the blue sky.

We walked on slowly, and came out of the cool shade of the trees into the brightness and warmth of the sun; the bay was in front of us. There was the sea-weedy smell of the beach, the taste of salt on my lips, and the murmur of faraway waves.

We stood by the granite wall, looking all around. The gulls soared overhead, the tide was very low, the sea far down the beach. There, on the rocks to the right, was the little tower, with the wall around, which everyone called the 'Cup And Saucer,' rather than Fort Grey the real name, because it looked just like a teacup inside a saucer.

Mam said, "The Germans have guns on the Cup and Saucer, and there are guns on the cliffs on the other side of the beach." We looked and looked, but could only see the trees, and the grey granite walls. I felt quite disappointed.

We went down the slipway and left our shoes by the wall. I hoped we would be able to go in the sea and swim. I walked on the sand, and it tickled my toes, and then picked up yellow shells. Jacques paddled and splashed in the pools, then ran in circles faster and faster.

As we neared the sea Mum suddenly stood still and said, "Listen."

We all stood still listening intently.

There was a plane, I knew that it wasn't German, the engines didn't make the distinctive, 'thrum, thrum' sound which we knew so well.

I looked at Jacques, and he looked at me. We knew that it must be a British plane, and that meant danger.

The sound grew louder and louder. There was the plane; we could see it flying low across the bay towards us. Suddenly Mum flung down the shrimping net, picked me up and threw me on the beach with such force it was difficult to breathe. My face was in some water, I was choking, Mum's body was covering me for protection, but that made it almost impossible to move. I couldn't see anything, and wondered what was happening to Jacques.

The roar of the plane's engines as it flew low overhead intensified, and there was the sound of guns firing, thundering, and roaring all around us. The sound of the engines receded into the distance, and the gunfire ceased.

I could hear Mum's rapid breathing, and could feel my own heart thumping; I was choking and spluttering, trying to get my breath.

I saw Jacques emerging from underneath Mam as we got up. Mum and Mam were shaking, their faces quite white. The sun was still shining, the beach looked the same, but now it was a place of danger.

We held hands and ran to the slip.

"We won't ever go on a beach again until this awful war ends, just think we could all have been killed," Mum said.

As we walked back up the lane Jacques giggled, and whispered, "Your Grandmother almost squashed me."

I laughed, and whispered back, "Mum almost drowned me, but they were both brave keeping us safe from bullets."

A few days after our visit to the Cup and Saucer Mum said, "Because you were so brave the other day Dad and I are taking you, and Jacques, to Town for a special treat."

We couldn't imagine what the treat could be, there was nothing much to buy, most of the shops were empty. If there was anything that had come from France we would have to queue for hours.

"I don't want to queue do you?" I asked.

Jacques shook his head, and looked gloomy, he really hated shopping.

After dinner we set off on our bikes, and at last came to the Gaumont Cinema. On top of the door was an enormous picture of Hitler.

Jacques whispered, "I always want to laugh at his moustache."

"Yes," I whispered back.

We both knew it was dangerous to say anything like that out loud.

Then we caught sight of a poster; it said 'The Wizard Of Oz.'

"That's what we're going to see," said Dad.

That was so exciting; we'd never been to a cinema before.

Dad bought the tickets. We went in, and an usherette led us to our seats. There was a rope dividing the cinema in half. There were Germans sitting behind us, and Guernsey people in our half.

We sat down, and looking around saw there was gold on the walls, and deep crimson velvet curtains in front.

"I bet Buckingham Palace is as grand as this," I said.

Jacques shook his head, "It's just like the Palace Of Versailles, I know because I've been there."

As the lights were lowered the curtains parted, and we saw that the film was in colour. It was a wonderful story, about Dorothy, who had magic red shoes. There was a tin man, a straw man, a lion and Toto the dog.

We were all sorry when the film was over.

"Can we come again?" I pleaded.

"It's not very likely said Dad, "most films are for adults, and they're usually in German."

And sure enough, we never did.

The 'Cup and Saucer' and the beach where the children were in great danger.

The Gaumont cinema where the children saw the Wizard of Oz.

'V' FOR VICTORY
Chapter 11

The next few days were boring after all the excitement. During the next few weeks we didn't see much of Mr. Max, but if we passed his house, and he was in the garden, he would come to the gate and give us a biscuit. Sometimes we'd wait hoping he would come out, but nothing really interesting happened.

It all changed when Grandpa told me about a broadcast from the B.B.C. Programme for Occupied Europe.

"Winston Churchill wants every one, in all the countries occupied by the Germans to draw the letter 'V' everywhere," he sounded really excited. "We can also make the letter 'V' in Morse code, which is three dots and a dash, and that can be done with a torch, or by making the sound by knocking.

The 'V' stands for victory for the Allies, and means that we will never be conquered."

The very next day Jacques and I saw an enormous 'V' painted on the wall at La Villette, which is just around the corner, and we knew the Germans would be mad.

When Uncle Bill called he knocked on the door with three little knocks, and a bang. I did the same when calling for Jacques. It was our secret signal; we would say da, da, da, dum if there was anything confidential to say.

It became more and more exciting. 'V' signs were appearing on walls everywhere. One day Grandmamma brought some books back from the Guille-Allèz Library, and as she opened one some 'V's', cut out of paper, fluttered to the ground.

"This'll show the Jerries," Grandpa said delightedly. Do you know they say there are   'V' for Victory In Europe signs all over the continent?"

I found a box of chalks in my toy box.

"Come on," I said to Jacques, " "let's go out and find a smooth wall and draw a "V."

As we went up the lane we saw Mr. Max going into his gate. Quick as lightening I hid the box behind my back.

"A fine day, yah?" he said.

We nodded in agreement, and hurried away.

We came to a big wall. We each took a piece of chalk, and started drawing the biggest 'V' we could. Suddenly, around the corner, came Dad.

I felt a bit scared; he was so angry. He grabbed our hands and we hurried home. He went to the cupboard, and took out a newspaper.

" Now read what it says aloud"

We both read: "Any persons found marking walls with 'V' signs or insults against the German Armed Forces are liable to be shot.

A reward will be paid to any persons giving information that will lead to the arrest of these offenders.

G. V. Schmettow

General German Military Government."

Dad frowned, "Now do you understand this is not a joke, or a game? It's extremely dangerous."

"Da, da, da, dum," Jacques whispered when we were in the garden, "What a pity he caught us, we'd have drawn the best 'V' signs ever. Still, it might have been a bit dangerous."

A few days later, when I as at Westwood, Grandpa was reading the Evening Press, "Well the Jerries are crafty, I'll give them that," he exclaimed.

I leant over his shoulder and read,

"V"---GERMAN VICTORY ON ALL FRONTS

I carried on reading; 'the 'V' signs mean victory for Germany. There are 'V' signs all over the continent. In Holland, hundreds of thousands of people are walking about with a little "v" brooch in orange colours. In France there is a giant 'V' on the Eiffel Tower. In Belgium all cars, lorries, tramways and steam engines have the letter 'V' at the front; in fact, everywhere there is the 'V' sign. And then in capital letters,

"V IS THE SIGN WORN AND DISPLAYED WITH THE CERTAIN CONFIDENCE OF A GERMAN VICTORY ON ALL FRONTS."

"Well that's the end of that," said Grandpa.

Sure enough he was right. The next day, as we cycled along the Grange on our way to Town, there on a wall was an enormous 'V' surrounded by laurel leaves, which the Germans had painted.

Soon there were lots of 'V's painted by the Germans, but no one else bothered.

Anyway, we still used it as our secret signal, and the B.B.C. always started all their broadcasts to Occupied Countries with music, and a drum made the 'V' sound as the opening notes.

Grandpa told us that the music was the first bars of Beethoven's fifth symphony, but we never heard the rest of the music.

ATTENTION—WARNING

Any persons found marking walls
with 'V' signs or insults against
the German Armed Forces
are liable to be shot.

A reward will be paid
to any persons giving information
that will lead to the arrest
of these offenders.

G. V. Schmettow
General,
German Military Government

A 'V' sign painted by the Germans and repainted over the years.

RULES AND MORE RULES
Chapter 12

The excitement of the 'V' signs soon ended, but everyone grumbled because the Germans were making more and more rules.

"I don't believe it," Dad said with horror, "we've got to hand in our wireless sets, and if we don't there'll be terrible punishments," he paused, "but I think I'll chance it, and find somewhere to hide the set."

"Don't be so stupid," Mum exclaimed, "you could be sent to prison in Germany or France."

"The Germans say they will give the sets back," Jacques said trying to cheer us up.

"And pigs might fly," Dad retorted angrily.

After the set had gone the cottage seemed empty and silent because the wireless had always been on. Mum and Dad missed the news most of all. They grumbled that they didn't know what was happening in the war, and didn't believe what the Germans told us because it was just propaganda.

The next thing that happened was that there were German road signs instead of the English ones. Jacques was pleased, because they were like the ones in France, but Grandpapa was furious.

"It's not only new signs," he said, "we've all got to ride on the right hand side of the road. What a cheek, we've always made our own rules. You mark my words, there'll be accidents."

We didn't find it too difficult riding on the right, until the day Jacques and I were cycling to Westwood. We came to a T-junction at Burnt Lane and saw the red triangle, which meant, 'Caution Main Road.'

Jacques was in front when around the corner appeared a fat soldier on a bike, and there was a collision. The German fell into the hedge in a mass of stinging nettles, and Jacques fell into the road. I crashed into both of them.

The soldier was furious. He screamed and shouted in German, waving his fist.

He became redder and redder in the face. He grabbed Jacques, hitting and shaking him.

I was terrified, but picked up Jacques's bike and thrust it at him He held the handlebars and managed to jump on. My bike was lying on the other side of the road, I grabbed it, and we cycled away as fast as we could.

We could hear the German still yelling. I thought he might fire his pistol, but at last we arrived safely at Westwood. My chin and forehead were grazed, and so were our knees. Grandmamma was not sympathetic.

"You must look where you are going, stay on the right, and use your brakes," she scolded as she bathed our cuts. "You're very lucky children; people have been shot for doing less."

"Your Gran's right," Jacques said on the way home, "The Germans are dangerous. I think we should keep away from Mr. Max."

Then he laughed, "I'm really pleased that fat German fell in the stinging nettles."

THE DOCTOR
Chapter 13

The war had gone on so long it was getting harder and harder to get the things we needed just to live. Most things had to come by boat from France, and that wasn't easy because the boats were in danger from planes, and submarines. Much of what did arrive was for the Germans, and there wasn't much for us.

Our clothes and shoes were wearing out, and the shops were empty. Every evening we looked in the Press, which had 'For Sale,' 'Exchange,' and 'Wanted' columns. Most people preferred looking in the Exchange Column, finding all kinds of things they wanted in exchange for what they could spare. Sometimes there would be clothes, or shoes, someone had outgrown for me or Jacques.

Jacques and I always read the Exchange Column, and I sometimes copied some of the advertisements in a notebook because they made me laugh, and I liked to imagine the people who advertised.

On the thirty first of December 1943 I copied, 'Manure for parsnips,' Mrs Le Page. Jacques laughed, "It's going to be smelly in her house, I'd rather have the parsnips."

Next I copied, '1 gallon of good lamp oil for cycle tyre,' Mrs Corbet, and we both decided it would be better to sit in the dark, and be able to go out on a bike.

When we read the next advertisements Jacques said, "My grandmother would never do this, she thinks a clean house is the most important thing in the whole world, and he read '1 new sweeping brush, 1 new scrubbing brush for a fowl old or young, apply Williams.' He laughed even more, she doesn't say dead or alive."

But as the months passed the column which became the longest was the Wanted Column, as everything people owned, and which they had once taken for granted, wore out.

The biggest problem however was we weren't getting much food, and I kept getting boils, and, even worse, mouth ulcers.

One day I was outside sitting on the hedge when Mr. Max walked towards me.

"You are sad?" he asked.

I guessed he could see I'd been crying because of the pain, so I opened my mouth wide and pointed.

"Come," he said, when he saw the red ulcers covering my gums, and the inside of my mouth.

We went into his front room, which was the surgery. I had a good look around. There were cupboards, and an examination couch. He went to a cupboard, and took a bottle with what looked like a rubber ball at the side.

"Open mouth," he ordered.

I opened my mouth as wide as possible, and he squeezed the ball. There was a spray of liquid in my mouth, and the pain disappeared.

He filled a medicine bottle with pink liquid, took my hand and we walked home.

He knocked on the door. When Mum opened it she looked astonished to see me holding the hand of a German, who was holding out a bottle of medicine.

As we went into the kitchen I explained what had happened.

"One spoon in a glass of water," Mr. Max said, pointing to the bottle, "then move medicine to wash mouth."

When Jacques came home I told him what had happened.

"Weren't you scared that he was poisoning you?"

"The ulcers hurt so much I didn't care."

"I'll go to thank him," Dad said when we told him about Mr. Max.

He was smiling when he returned, "He seems a good sort. He's missing his family so I've told him to call here when he wants."

It wasn't long before Mr. Max kept coming to chat. He talked incessantly about his family. He told us he worked as a medical orderly with Dr. Hodeige, who lived at Medacombra, and I realized he was the officer we saw the day the German's came to live in our lane. He said he was a very good doctor, and he looked after the patients really well.

I knew Mr. Max's house was the surgery, and he told us when there was fighting it would become a field station, where the wounded would come for help.

In bed that night it was terrifying to realize that Mr. Max expected that there would be fighting in Guernsey, and I wondered if there was anywhere we could hide.

Quite often we saw the Doctor striding up the path to the surgery. He was tall, wore a black uniform, and highly polished boots, and looked very smart. We seemed to be invisible because he totally ignored us.

One night we were suddenly woken up by the wailing sounds of the air raid sirens. As we hurried downstairs to the cupboard under the stairs I could see the searchlights moving across the sky, trying to find the British bombers.

When we were inside Mum lit the candle, while I cuddled Tibs as the bombs fell, and the guns roared, and my heart thumped. I thought of Freyda, because Max had told us there was terrible bombing in Germany.

We all sang as loudly as we could, to drown the noise, but it didn't, it was much louder than thunder. I wished Jacques was with us, instead of in the cupboard next door, on the other side of the wall.

At last the raid stopped, and when the all clear sounded we went back to our freezing cold beds."

The next morning Jacques came round.

"Isn't it strange," I said, "we're frightened because the British bomb us, and Max is frightened because they bomb Freyda,"

"They're not bombing us, they're bombing the Germans who shouldn't be here, and the Germans are bombing everybody in England, so it's their fault," Jacques said decisively.

I frowned, "Well it doesn't make any sense to me, why do adults want to fight, and kill children?"

Jacques looked puzzled, and shook his head.

We were getting to like Mr. Max more and more. Once he gave Mum some sugar, she stewed apples, and put oatmeal on top, and he shared the delicious pudding. It was lovely to have real sugar instead of saccharine. I cleaned my plate with my finger so I wouldn't miss a crumb.

One day he called us when we were playing.

"I give you to-day a treat, it is Freyda's favourite."

He gave us each a bowl of sour milk, which had set, with brown sugar sprinkled on the top. We sat at the table, and each took a spoonful. I had to try hard not to make a face, and Jacques seemed to find it difficult to swallow, but in the end we managed to eat it all up.

"Only people who are really hungry would eat that," Jacques said, when we got outside.

I nodded, " I liked the sugar. Do you think Freyda really likes it?"

We both felt a bit doubtful.

One afternoon Jacques was having tea with us because Grandmère was visiting her cousin.

"My throat," he suddenly gasped, and pointed to his neck.

"We must get help," Mum said.

She held Jacques's hand and hurried out. I followed as she ran to Max's house, and knocked on the door. When Max heard what had happened he spoke calmly, and Jacques didn't look quite as scared.

Jacques was getting onto the examination couch when there was the sound of the front door opening, then footsteps in the hall, and Dr Hodeige walked in.

Mum started to tell the story again, I felt very apprehensive as he looked so forbidding.

He didn't smile; he looked stern.

"Open the mouth, "he said, holding Jacques's chin in his hand, and tipping back his head.

He peered into his mouth, then turned, and spoke to Max in German. Max opened a drawer, and gave him an instrument, which he held to push down Jacques's tongue.

Jacques sounded as if he was going to be sick.

"Keep the mouth open wide, and do not move." The doctor spoke sternly.

I watched as he put a shiny instrument down Jacques's throat, and pulled out a long, pointed husk.

"Be more careful in future," he said holding up the husk.

" Say thank you to the Doctor for being so kind," Mum said.

"Thank you," mumbled Jacques.

But I didn't think the doctor was particularly kind.

"Cor, that hurt," Jacques whispered when we got home, and spat blood out onto his hanky.

When Dad came back from work Mum told him all that had happened.

"I thought Max would get into trouble for helping us," she said, "but they're both kind men."

I wasn't too sure.

Dad didn't seem in the least surprised at what had happened to Jacques.

"Every slice of bread has husks. I've taken people to hospital to get them removed. Sometimes people have to have anaesthetics to get them out.

You were very brave Jacques." I nodded in agreement.

The next day Jacques was still whispering. I asked him what Grandmère had said.

"I just said that my throat hurt. I didn't say anything about the Doctor or Max, because she'd have been furious. She hates all Germans, and will never trust any of them."

THE LONG WINTER
Chapter 14

When I was at school it was difficult not to mention Mr Max. Jacques and I knew that had to be a secret; if anyone found out we wouldn't have any friends because everyone else believed that he was an enemy.

It was hard having a secret we couldn't share with our friends, but we liked school because the war seemed further way when we were in the classroom.

Then one cold wet afternoon, not long before my birthday, Jacques and I arrived home from school, and were surprised to find the fire nearly out, and there was a feeble call from upstairs.

I went up and Mum was in bed. Her face was as white as the sheet, and as she breathed there was a wheezing sound.

"I'm not very well," she whispered, " Daddy will get your tea."

I went down and put wood on the fire. The house felt strange and empty without Mum bustling about.

When Dad came back Jacques went home, and we had black bread, and cheese we'd smuggled home from the farm for supper.

On my way up to bed I took Mum a cup of blackberry leaf tea.

"Don't worry," she whispered, "I'll be fine in the morning."

But she wasn't, and when I came back from school Mam Camp was in the kitchen, taking care of everything.

"Doctor Rose has been and seen your Mother," she said anxiously, "he says she's very ill with pneumonia, but you don't need to worry, I'm sure she'll be better soon."

It's strange, I thought, how everyone says not to worry, when they all look worried sick themselves.

Jacques came in and we sat by the fire.

"Mum's got pneumonia," I said, "I've read about pneumonia in storybooks, usually people die if they get it, even children."

Jacques looked serious, "I've heard of pneumonia too, but your Mum's strong, I'm sure she'll be all right."

I wasn't at all sure, but all the same felt a bit more cheerful.

During the next few days the house didn't feel like home, it seemed full of shadows, and whispering. I wasn't allowed to see Mum, they said she was resting.

Dr Rose called night and morning.

"Mrs. Renouf has to drink as much fluid as possible, and to be kept warm with a fire day and night," he said.

We didn't know how we were going to do that, because we didn't have much fuel left. But friends and neighbours must have heard that Mum was very ill, and came bringing gifts of food, and, best of all, coal.

One morning there was a knock on the door, and when we opened it Max was standing there, holding a basket.

"I hear Mrs. Renouf is ill, and I have brought some things."

When we opened the basket there was a jelly, and a packet of real tea.

Mam took up a cup of tea, and some jelly. When she came down she didn't look happy.

"She drank a little of the tea, but only managed a teaspoon of jelly," she paused, "I don't like, or trust, any Germans, but I must say he does seem very kind."

That afternoon I heard Mam talking to Dad in the kitchen, and crept near and listened.

"Dr. Rose has been, and he's very, very concerned, she's not making the progress he hoped. He says the next few days are critical."

I was so scared it was difficult to breathe, my mouth was dry, it was impossible to swallow. I just couldn't imagine what it would be like if Mum wasn't here.

Suddenly the door opened. Dad must have guessed I'd been listening, and knew how frightened I was.

He smiled, "Don't worry, Mum's a fighter, everything's going to be all right." But it didn't feel in the least bit right.

Later, as we were putting up the blackout, and had just switched on the light we heard someone coming up the path. We opened the door, and Dr. Hodeige was standing on the doorstep.

"I hear from Max that Mrs. Renouf is ill, perhaps I can help?"

Dad took him upstairs into the bedroom. I sat on the top stair on the landing, and listened. There was the sound of the men's voices, then silence.

When they came out I moved back into the shadows.

"She is seriously ill, I will send Max with some medicine, see she takes it," the doctor said.

"I hope we're doing the right thing," Dad said after he left, "at least it can't do any harm."

A short time later there was another knock. This time it was Max, with a bottle of medicine, and a bowl of junket.

He came in, put the things on the table, gave a big grin and said, "Do not worry."

Next morning when I woke up Mam told me that Dr. Hodeige had come back twice, to check how Mum was.

The next night he was there when I went to bed.

In the morning Dad said that he had stayed until after midnight, when the crisis had passed, and that meant Mum should get better.

I skipped to school that morning, and in the evening was allowed to go into the bedroom. Mum's voice was still a whisper, but she beckoned. I curled up on her bed; we didn't talk because that made the coughing worse. I held her hand until she fell asleep.

It was warm and cosy. The flickering flames in the grate made shadows on the wall, and it felt safe.

"I can see your Mum's getting better, you're smiling," Jacques said when we met next morning.

I grinned even more, "Yes, thanks to Dr. Hodeige, our house feels like home. I was scared of him, but now he's a real friend."

CHRISTMAS 1943
Chapter 15

After Mum got better the days flew past, and it was my birthday, and to my astonishment there were two presents. One was a necklace of pink coral that I recognised from Grandmama's jewel box, the second a watch from Mum and Dad, I guessed they had got it from an advertisement in the Press, and wondered what they'd given in exchange.

We even had a special breakfast, instead of the usual porridge we had boiled eggs, my birthday present from Mam and Papa Camp.

In the afternoon Jacques was invited to tea. At four o'clock there was a knock on the door. Jacques was standing on the step holding a present. It was quite big, and wrapped in newspaper.

"Come on in, it's freezing," I said pulling him inside.

Jacques looked impatient, " Just you see what I've got for you, I made it myself."

I took the parcel, it felt heavy and knobbly. As the paper came off it was some sort of animal, made out of wood. Looking more closely I decided that it was a horse.

Jacques was smiling, "I found the wood in your vinery, it was part of a branch that had blown down from a tree. Your Dad let me use the saw to cut off what I wanted. He lent me a penknife to carve with, and some sandpaper to make the wood smooth. Grandmère was a bit worried at first, she was certain I would cut myself."

I looked at the carving, and could see a face, the ears, the eyes and the nostrils.

"It can stand on it's own," Jacques said proudly.

I stared hard, and could see it was a carthorse. It looked as if it was pulling a heavy plough across a field.

"Do you like him?" Jacques sounded a bit anxious.

" Oh yes, he's my very best present."

It was a lovely birthday. Mum was still quite weak and lay on the sofa, but she was much better. There was even a birthday tea, which Dad had prepared. There were potato cakes and a sponge cake, of course there wasn't any icing, but there were the candles from other birthdays, which were now half burnt down. I hoped the war would end soon or there might not be any candles left to burn.

After tea we got out the dartboard, and I actually managed to hit the bull's eye. Then we had a treasure hunt, and the prize we all shared was a bar of Fry's chocolate cream. I guessed it came from the Black Market, it must have been at least three years old, and the chocolate was speckled with white mould, but it was delicious, and we all ate it as slowly as we could to make it last.

That night in bed I looked at the wooden horse standing on the dressing table, and decided that it had been a lovely birthday. Best of all, Mum was here to share it.

Then there were only a few more days to Christmas. Jacques and I took over decorating the house.

On Christmas Eve Mam and Papa Camp came and brought in baskets of things, which were whisked out of sight.

"Tomorrow Jacques and Grandmère are coming to dinner," Dad said.

On Christmas morning there was something at the bottom of the bed, it was a stocking! I didn't want to disturb Mum so I opened it. Inside were crayons, a book of drawing paper, and a book, "What Katy Did."

As it was very early I fell asleep. When I woke up there was a delicious smell, I sniffed, and remembered what it was, bacon!

I ran down and Mum was sitting at the table.

"Papa hid one of the piglets from the Germans," Dad said as he put the food on the table, "and when it was big enough it was killed, and he made bacon. It's been hidden at the farm for months."

At dinnertime Grandmère and Jacques came, and we had a chicken, with lots of vegetables. All this was from Mam and Papa. I knew why; they were happy, Mum was almost better.

"We have some presents for both of you," Mum said, after we'd cleared up, and gave us two parcels each.

I had a white angora jumper; and recognized the wool; it had been made from Mum's best cardigan. My second present was a book called, 'Little Women.'

When Jacques opened his first present he gasped in astonishment, because inside was a large penknife.

"Be careful," warned Dad, "I know you like carving, but the blades are very sharp."

Jacques nodded, and opened the second present, inside was a book called 'Black Beauty.'

He grinned, "Thank you, two perfect presents, my very own knife, and a book which looks as if it's about horses. I love horses."

That evening when Jacques had gone home we sat in the firelight, and I was so happy that the three of us were together, and Mum was well.

On New Year's Day there was a knock on the door, and Dr Hodeige and Max came in.

"We have for you brought a bottle of schnapps to drink a toast to the New Year," Max said, "and some lemonade for Marianne, and some biscuits."

Dad brought out glasses.

"To the health of Mrs. Renouf," said the doctor, and every one drank. Then he said, "A Happy New Year to us all," and we drank again.

"Another toast," Max said, "To the end of war," but I noticed no one said whom they wanted to win.

TROUBLE
Chapter 16

On the first day of term after Christmas Jacques was waiting at the gate, he was grinning, "There's one good thing about electricity being rationed, we don't start school until ten o'clock, and I stay in bed for ages to keep warm."

I nodded, "And what's even better school finishes early."

We waved goodbye, and I skipped up the hill, thinking how good it would be to see my friends. When the bell rang we went to the classroom. To our surprise Madam Marie Helene wasn't waiting for us, and there were no pictures on the walls, and no work waiting on our desks.

We were so surprised no one said anything, and then suddenly there was the sound of footsteps and the swish of Reverend Mother's long robes as she walked in.

"Go to your desks children, and sit down," she said.

There was the shuffle of feet, and we all sat up straight, waiting.

"I have some sad news for you. In the holidays Madam Marie Helene died from pneumonia. We will say a prayer for her, and then you must go home and tell your parents, and come back tomorrow for her funeral."

"I've never been to a funeral before, I wonder what happens," I said, as we walked down the drive.

Everyone shook their heads, they didn't know either.

When I reached home I wondered if Madam Marie Helene would have got better if Dr Hodeige had seen her. Then I remembered how scary it had been when Mum was ill, and ran into the kitchen, and was so relieved to see that she really was there, busy sweeping the floor.

The next day was grey and miserable, everyone was quiet, and we tip-toed into school. We didn't take off our coats, and were sent straight into the chapel. I felt a bit scared.

There was the smell of incense, and the coffin was in front of the altar. It didn't seem possible that Madam Marie Helene was inside, it didn't feel real. I could almost believe that when we went back into our classroom she'd be there, smiling, pleased to see us.

There were lots of prayers, and the priest said that although every one was sad, we should also feel glad that Madam Marie Helene was happy in heaven, but the hymns and music were mournful.

As the coffin was carried out we followed in a procession to the Convent graveyard. The day was dark and gloomy, with gusts of wind and drops of rain falling. The only sounds were the crunch of gravel under our feet, and the wind in the trees. Nobody said a word.

When we reached the graveyard the grave was ready, and very, very, deep. The priest said some more prayers, and the coffin was lowered into the grave with ropes.

Afterwards Reverend Mother said, "Go back to your homes, and return tomorrow."

Walking away it seemed sad and lonely leaving Madam Marie Helene all alone in the dark.

For the next few weeks we didn't have a teacher, and spent all our time silent reading.

"It's so boring," I grumbled to Jacques, "I wish we could have a teacher of our own."

"Grandmère says be careful what you wish, it might come true," Jacques replied.

"That's so stupid," I retorted, but a few weeks later discovered what Grandmère meant.

On a Monday morning we walked into our classroom, Reverend Mother and a lady were waiting

"This is Miss Sanders," Reverend Mother said, "she is your new teacher. I want to hear that you are all obedient, and working hard."

I looked at Miss Sanders, and noticed that although she smiled with her mouth, her eyes didn't smile at all.

Reverend Mother left, and everyone was quiet.

"Get out your reading books," Miss Sanders said.

We all tried to be quick, in fact I tried so hard the lid of the desk slipped, and banged down.

Miss Sanderson glared at me, "Any more of that nonsense and you will be kept in. Turn to page ten."

"Which page did she say?" whispered Jane.

Miss Sanders looked up.

"Ten," I whispered.

"I can see we have a trouble maker here," roared Miss Sanders.

She pulled a desk forward until it was right in front of her table, and she walked up, grabbed my arm, pulled me to the desk, and pushed me onto the seat.

"In future you will sit here where I can keep an eye on you."

"I really and truly hate and detest her," I told Jacques, "I don't think she likes children very much, she certainly doesn't like me, she says I'm stupid."

We spent hours writing in copybooks. There was a line of writing that said things like, ' Silence is golden,' then we had to copy it three times underneath, in ink, without any blots. No matter how hard I tried it always looked wrong, and that meant staying in at play-time."

Jacques looked sympathetic, "Well I'm jolly pleased I don't go to your school. I know, let's make up a game, we'll pretend she's a witch, and we capture her, and torture her, and put her in the boiler in the pit in the vinery."

It was a good game, but it didn't seem to make school any better.

One afternoon the classroom door opened, and Reverend Mother came in followed by a girl about our age.

"Children I want you to welcome Lesley, who is coming to join you," she said as we stood up."

Lesley turned out to be awful. She quickly became Miss Sanders pet. Worst of all she told tales, and we lost playtimes because of what she said. We decided that it was like having a spy in our midst.

All the lessons were boring now, and every thing seemed to go wrong for me. Instead of having pages of ticks in arithmetic there were pages of crosses.

My favourite lesson used to be composition. The first composition we had to write for Miss Sanders was about a naughty puppy.

I wrote, 'the puppy cautiously pushed open the door and soroptishously sneaked out with piece of meat.'

The teacher was walking around the room, reading what everyone was writing, and stopping and sticking her fingers in the back of anyone who made a mistake.

I could sense her standing behind me.

"What do these words say?" she asked.

"Cautiously and surreptitiously," I replied, knowing they were the right words, because Grandmamma always said, 'be cautious,' in any dangerous situation, and Mum always said, 'stop acting surreptitiously,' when we're tried to hide something.

"Don't use words you don't understand, and then don't write them until you can spell them correctly," Miss Sanders hissed.

She wrote 'surreptitiously' and 'cautiously' underneath the story, and said, "Stop writing your story, and write each word fifty times."

When the bell rang for playtime I was still writing the words, and had to stay in.

When everyone returned Miss Sanders took the book.

"Well, let's see if you have learnt from your mistakes, spell cautiously."

I hadn't realized that I was supposed to learn the words, and whispered. "Coshisly."

Miss Sanderson frowned, picked up the chalk and wrote, CAUTIOUSLY on the blackboard.

Now face the class and spell it properly.

"Caustioly," I muttered.

"Rubbish, you stupid child, try again."

Everyone started to giggle. I could feel my face getting redder and redder; and thought, I'm NOT going to cry.

I hesitated, "Corchisly," everyone laughed louder.

There was the sound of chalk on the board, and then Miss Sanderson said, "Well, let us see how well you spell surreptitiously."

"Suroptitsiuly."

Everyone laughed, even louder and louder.

"Again," said Miss Sanderson, and I could tell she was smiling her cruel smile; and knew she was really enjoying this.

I took a deep breath and spelt, "Sureptitiously."

No one laughed for a moment, wondering if that was right, until Miss Sanders shouted, "Rubbish," and then they all laughed again. Lesley laughed loudest of all.

Suddenly Miss Sanders was standing in front of me, "No painting for you this afternoon, you will write those words again, and this time make certain that you can spell them. Perhaps this will teach you not to be too big for your boots, and stop you showing off, but I must say that I have my doubts. I fear that you are incorrigible, if you know what that means."

When it was time to go home to dinner I hurried out, frightened that the others might still laugh at me. Hurrying down the drive there was the sound of running feet, and Jane caught me up.

"She's a pig, a real nasty pig. Everyone laughed because they were pleased she wasn't making fun of them."

I felt a bit happier, and when we were eating dinner asked, "What does incorrigible mean?"

Mum got out the dictionary, "It says, impossible to change what someone does, or the way they behave.

Why do you want to know?"

"It was just a word I heard," but inside I was thinking, good, there's no way she's going to change me.

I told Jacques about the horrible day, and said, "I won't write exciting stories any more. I'll write short stories with words that are easy to spell, and make up exciting ones in my head."

I used to sit and look at Miss Sanders and imagined her inside the boiler, in the pit, with the door bricked up, while she scratched and scrabbled, and pleaded to be let out; but I knew she would never get out, never for all eternity.

THE CHIMNEY
Chapter 17

"Anyone who has anything to do with the Germans is a collaborator!" Grandpa said."What does that mean?" I asked.

"It means being friends with the enemy, in other words a traitor."

It's lucky, I thought, he doesn't know about Dr. Hodeige, who sometimes came to our house because Mum was teaching him English.

One day when I came home Mum looked miserable.

"What's the matter?" I asked.

"Dr Hodeige is leaving Guernsey, to be the doctor in the island of Alderney."

I knew Mum was frightened of being ill again, and the doctor wouldn't be here to help her, and I felt worried too.

I think it good that he's going," Jacques said, " that leaves Max who comes to your house, but he comes at night so it's more secret. If Grandmère saw Germans coming to your house she wouldn't let me near you. She says she hates the German Hun; because they killed my Grandpère."

It was horrible thinking what Grandmamma and Grandpa would say if they knew that the Germans, their enemies, had been in our house, they would say we were traitors and collaborators.

"We have to keep it secret," I said, "especially at school, or they'll call us 'Jerry Lovers,' that's the worst name anyone can be called, worse than the most terrible swear word." Jacques nodded.

I really hated secrets now because they usually meant danger, which seemed to surround us more and more.

One day I had to go to the farm, and when I arrived Mam said, "I am making some butter. Can you keep watch for the Germans, so I can hide the churn if they come?"

From the time I was very small I'd liked watching Mam rocking the churn, with the swish, swish of milk, and the changing sound when the butter formed.

I'd watch as the butter was taken out and mixed with salt, then patted into shape with wooden patters, the little drops of water glistening on the bright, yellow surface.

I knew it was dangerous making butter now because it was forbidden to keep milk, every drop had to be taken to the dairy, but Papa always kept some back.

I even knew one of the secret hiding places for the butter and cheese, and that was a little shelf in the chimney.

I'd never kept watch before, so that was exciting. It was sunny and peaceful, and I went into the farmyard and climbed the wall that overlooked the road. The farm cat, Puss, jumped up purring and rubbing herself against me.

Suddenly there was the sound of lorries.

"The Germans are coming, the Germans are coming," I shouted as I ran in.

Mam quickly hid the churn in the cupboard. We waited, but no one came. I went out again to watch and listen, and this time was certain that there were marching feet coming nearer and nearer.

Once more I ran, as fast as possible, "They are coming. They are coming."

This time Mam went to look out of the door, there wasn't a German in sight.

"Don't bother about the Germans," she said, giving me a hug, "I know, in my bones, they aren't coming today. Go out and play, and see if there are any eggs."

I found two eggs in the stable where the hens were kept, and when I went in the churn

A Churn similar to the one used by Mam.

had disappeared. There was some butter on the table, and the rest was up the chimney.

I took some butter and the eggs home, and told Jacques what had happened

"Well, you're daft," he said, "I'd have waited until the Germans came into sight."

I frowned, "Bet you wouldn't, that would be much too risky. Anyway the danger's past."

But the next day I realised it hadn't.

It was during playtime, and we were having our mid-morning snacks. Mum had given me some bread, spread with the delicious farm butter."

"Your Mum's going to be mad with you," Iris said, "when she finds out how much butter you put on your bread, it looks like a whole ration."

I was just going to say, "she spread it", then realized that could be very dangerous, someone might come to investigate where the butter had come from.

So I nodded, "I'm going to get into trouble, I'll probably have to go to bed without tea."

"Perhaps you've got extra butter, and that's illegal." Lesley said, staring at me.

She turned and walked into school. We followed, and I stuck my tongue out, everyone laughed. Lesley looked around suspiciously, and I knew that I had to be more careful in future.

The farm wall where Marianne kept watch for the Germans.

SECRETS
Chapter 18

Life was becoming more dangerous and one of the worst things of all, for me, was there was a secret that I couldn't share, not even with Jacques.

It all started after the 'V' for victory signs. A notice appeared in the Press saying that all wireless sets had to be handed in. There would be severe punishments if any were kept.

Dad wanted to hide our set, but Mum was frightened.

"It's too dangerous, the punishments are awful."

So the set went, and the house seemed quiet and empty. Dad was really miserable now he couldn't listen to the B.B.C. News, and tell us about the fighting in the world, because the Germans weren't winning as many battles, and the English and American soldiers were doing well.

One day he came home and he was grinning.

"I must say there are some brave Guernsey men who are risking everything for us." He pulled out a sheet of paper, and at the top were the letters. G.U.N.S. "Guernsey Underground News Service," he said. Some people have a hidden wireless set, and listen to the news every night and print what they hear in this paper. It's not only dangerous for them, if the Germans found someone reading it they would be punished."

"Don't bring it here," pleaded Mum, "it's too risky."

"I only see it occasionally," Dad grumbled, "it's difficult to get hold of."

A few weeks later Dad was pushing his bike up the path, and I saw that there was a box on the carrier. He brought it in and locked the front and back doors, and then he pulled the curtain so no one could look in. "This isn't a wireless set," he said, putting the box on the table, "it's the next best thing, it's a crystal set."

When he opened the box I was astonished. There was a small wooden board, with what looked like a little piece of shiny rock. There was a bit of wire, with a thinner wire at the end that could be moved on a swivel. There were two headphones that were made from the part of the ordinary telephone you hold to your ear.

"This is a crystal," Dad said pointing at the rock. Then he pointed at the thin wire, "and this is called the cat's whisker. You have to tickle the crystal with the cat's whisker, and it becomes a wireless."

I put on the headphones, and wiggled the wire. At first there was nothing, then to my amazement, some music. I kept on fiddling with the wire and suddenly heard, bom, bom, bom, bommm. I jumped with excitement, it was the 'V,' for Victory sign, and a voice said, "This is the B.B.C. In Europe, here is the News."

"It's a magic wireless set," I whispered as I took off the headphones.

"I don't know about magic," said Dad, "but it's special and dangerous. If it's found I'll be sent to prison, I might even be sent to a camp on the continent. It's even possible that I could be shot, so you must promise never to tell anyone."

"Not even Jacques?"

"Not even Jacques. Do you promise?"

"Yes," I whispered.

Mum looked scared, "Having G.U.N.S in the house was bad enough, but this is more dangerous." Dad gave her a hug, "Don't worry, we'll make certain it can't be found."

" The crystal set is in this room, see if you can find it," Mum said the next day, when I came home from school. I searched everywhere, and at last had to give up. Mum got out of her chair, took off the cushion she was sitting on, and underneath was a sheet of wood, which looked like part of the seat, she lifted it off and there was the crystal set."

"I'd never have found it," I gasped.

Whenever I had the chance I'd listen to the set. I liked music and singing best, but sometimes there would be Lord Haw Haw. He always began, 'Garmany calling, Garmany calling,' Dad told me Lord Haw Haw wasn't his real name, it was the name the British people had given him, because he talked in such a posh voice.

Grandpa said that he was a British traitor, who worked for Germany, and gave Propaganda talks saying that the Germans were winning the war, but I liked listening to him because his voice made me laugh.

That winter I was often ill, and had to stay home. As a treat Mum let me listen to the set in bed. One programme had lots of old Music Hall songs, and the singer sang:

"I'm Enery' the eighth I am I am,

I am married to the widow next door,

She's been married seven times before,

And every one was an 'Enery,' never a Willy or a Sam,

And as my name is 'Enery,'

'Enery' the eighth I am."

Grandpa's name was Henry, so I thought the song particularly funny, and by the end of the programme could sing it all the way through.

When I went back to school I sang it to my friends, and they laughed.

"Where did you hear that?" Iris asked.

Without thinking I said, "I heard it on the crystal, then stopped, adding my Gran sings it," but my heart went thump, thump.

I saw Lesley staring at me.

A few days later, on Saturday, it was cold and Jacques was out with Grandmère, and I was bored.

"Get the set out of the chair," Mum said, "and put the cushions back and come and listen in the kitchen, while I get dinner."

I was just putting on the headphones when there was the bang of the gate. I looked out of the front window and saw, to my horror, two soldiers walking up the path.

"Mum, there are Germans coming." I whispered,
Mum looked scared.

" If they knock take as long as you can unlocking the door."

There was the sound of hammering on the doorknocker. I ran calling out, "I'm coming, I'm coming," and fiddled with the bolts as slowly as possible, and twisted the key.

"Raus! Raus!" a German shouted.

I guessed that meant hurry up.

Slowly I unlocked the door. One German pushed me aside, while the other was looking through the front room window.

A soldier went to the kitchen door, gave Mum a piece of paper and shouted, "We search."

Mum looked very white, but her voice didn't sound scared as she said, "Carry on."

Then, to my surprise, I saw she was holding the handle of my doll's pram and my doll; Elizabeth Anne and Teddy were inside.

" Take your pram and carry on playing in the garden," she said.

I almost said, I'm much too old to play with a pram, but instead did as I was told.

Standing in the garden there was the sound of doors opening and shutting, and occasional bangs and bumps, then the front door opened, and the soldiers strode past me.

When I went in the drawers and cupboard doors were open, and the contents strewn all over the floor. Then I saw that the cushion from the chair had been thrown aside. The piece of wood that hid the crystal set was on the floor.

I stared at Mum in horror.

"They found the set, what will happen to us?"

Mum smiled, "No, I couldn't hide the set in the chair, a German was looking in through the window. Look in your pram."

I lifted up Elizabeth Anne; there was nothing. Then I lifted up one of the sections that covered the base, and there was the set.

When Dad came in we told him what had happened.

He turned pale, "We've been so fortunate, I'll make a better hiding place at the back of the cupboard.

It's very strange; the Germans don't waste their time searching randomly. Max has told me that they have anonymous letters, telling them who has a hidden set, and often exactly where it is hidden."

I was horrified, "Guernsey people wouldn't do that, would they?"

"Most Guernsey people help one another, and some are really brave, but I'm sorry to say there are a few who do mean things, but no one knows about our set, so this is a mystery."

I felt shivery inside.

Lesley that must have guessed, and told her mother and father, then they told the Germans.

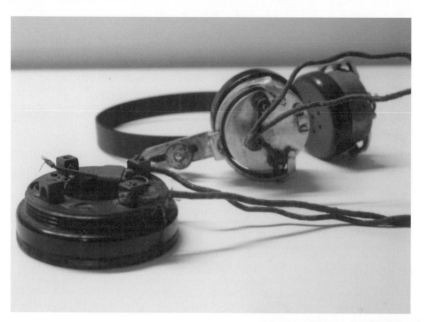

A crystal set.

The teddy and doll that hid the set.

SCOTTY
Chapter 19

After our house was searched everything seemed to go wrong. The problem was there wasn't enough to eat. We were always hungry. As soon as we came home from school Jacques and I ate what we called 'pink bread,' it was really raw swede, but it was sweet, and filled us up.

We were pleased to get food from the farm, what we hated was having to take Scotty, the dog, out for his walk. He was smellier than ever, even more bad tempered, and terribly thin.

One day we came home exhausted, it had been raining nearly all day, and we were soaked.

"Everything's wet, I grumbled to Mum. "We had to take Scotty. I wish the wretched dog had never been born."

The next day I was sorry I'd said that, because the telephone rang and it was Mam Camp.

"Come quickly, Scotty has disappeared."

We jumped on our bikes and cycled to the farm. Mam was waiting; we could see she'd been crying.

"It's my fault, I went to hang out the washing. I must have left the door ajar, because when I came back he'd gone."

I tried to be reassuring, "Don't worry, Jacques and I will find him."

But although we walked miles, and asked everyone we met if they'd seen a little, black Scotty dog, they all looked sad, and said they hadn't. It was clear he'd vanished without trace.

We stayed for tea, and had jacket potatoes, but Mam didn't eat anything.

Papa didn't look sad, he was angry.

"If I catch the thieves I'll give them something to remember. They come at night and milk my cows, they've killed one of my calves, all that was left was a pool of blood. Now they've eaten the dog."

"No one would eat Scotty," I protested.

"Starving men would," Papa said.

I knew that was true, and who they were.

Jacques and I'd been cycling in the lanes near Saint's Bay, when a straggling line of gaunt, haggard men, dressed in rags, some even had rags on their feet, came towards us.

We jumped off our bikes, and stood in the gateway to a field, and stared in amazement.

The men didn't seem aware of anything thing around them, they just shuffled along. There were two German soldiers guarding them, but they were walking at the back chatting, and occasionally shouting an order.

As they disappeared around the corner Jacques gave a big sigh.

"I'm really sorry for those people, they look so unhappy."

"Let's go home and ask Dad who they are, and if we can do anything to help them," I suggested.

When we arrived home we rushed in, and told Dad what we'd seen.

"Who are they?" asked Jacques.

"They are men from many countries conquered by the Germans," Dad replied, "and have been forced to come here to build huge defences to stop the British landing. They've no money, and they're given very little food, so at night they creep away from the camps, and steal; they're no more than slaves."

"Let's put out some food," I suggested.

Dad frowned, "We can't, it's strictly forbidden, we'd be severely punished if we did."

Then he pulled us both in front of him, and looked stern.

"You must not go anywhere near them, they're full of lice and disease. There's even been an outbreak of typhoid fever in Town, and that's an illness that kills.

Do you understand?"

We nodded reluctantly.

We didn't see the slaves very often. Mum said they went past the house early in the morning, on their way to their work on the cliffs, and came back late at night.

Every evening when I came home from school I looked at the ' Lost Column' in the Press, and read about dogs and cats that had disappeared, and the rewards offered for their return. I shivered, wondering if Tibby Puss would survive.

An advertisement for a lost pet. £5.00 was a lot of money.

A HOLIDAY
Chapter 20

I hated school more and more, and tried to keep away from Lesley, but she seemed to have eyes in the back of her head, and ears that heard the faintest whisper.

When the summer holiday arrived I said to Jacques, "Good, I won't have to see horrible Lesley, or detestable Miss Sanders for weeks and weeks."

I spoke too soon; I was astonished to see Lesley playing in our lane with her friend Muriel. Whenever Jacques and I went out they would whisper, point at us, and giggle.

"We have to be very careful," Jacques, said, "we mustn't go near Max's house, it would be terrible if they saw us talking to him."

I nodded, "We must watch when we bring food home from the farm, if our saddle bags are bulging they'll guess we're smuggling something."

Early one morning there was the clip clop of horse's hooves, and Papa was at the gate.

"Would you two like to come haymaking at Uncle Horace's farm?"

We nodded enthusiastically, and were soon on our way.

I loved going to Uncle Horace, he was Mum's brother, and lived on the farm where she grew up. He was lonely because his wife, and little boy had been evacuated. He didn't know what had happened for ages, because Red Cross letters took months and months to arrive, and you could only write twenty-five words, so baby Ann was quite big when he discovered she'd been born.

We trotted into the farmyard, and Uncle Horace waved as we jumped down. He spoke to Papa who went into the house.

"Good to see you," he said turning to us. "There was a heavy dew last night so the hay's a bit damp, we'll get it in after dinner. I've got to take some grain to the brewery so you can come."

He went into the stable, and came out leading a bullock pulling a cart. Jacques stared in astonishment.

"Let me introduce you," I said, " this is 'Adonis. Uncle Horace has trained him because there's too much work for Tommy the horse. Bulls can't wear a bridle and bit so that's why he has a yoke. Look, his feet are different from those of a horse, so he has two shoes on each foot, a large one and a little one."

We clambered onto the cart and sat at the front, and Adonis started off.

"He's a good beast," said Uncle Horace, "he pulls carts, and even ploughs. It's hard work for him because Guernsey bulls are small, but they make up for it in strength."

I started to laugh, remembering what I'd seen in the spring.

"It's really funny seeing Uncle Horace ploughing. Adonis and Tommy have to plough together, as Tommy is tall, and Adonis is short, Tommy walks in the furrow, while Adonis walks on the ridge. Next year you can come to see for yourself."

It was a slow journey, Adonis didn't hurry. As we drove along the front we both felt very important, Germans and civilians stopped and stared, and some waved.

We didn't get back until dinner time, and had a lovely meal of stew with lots of vegetables, and rhubarb and curds for pudding.

"Come on, time for work," Uncle Horace said when we'd finished.

In the field the hay was ready, it was golden, and perfectly dry. Tommy pulled the cart into the field. We helped rake up the hay and two men tossed it onto the cart with their pitchforks, and the load grew higher and higher.

When it was very high Uncle Horace said," We'll take the hay back, and store it in the barn."

He helped us to clamber to the top as Tommy started to walk. The hay was warm and soft, and smelled wonderful. The load swayed to and fro.

"It must feel like this on a boat," Jacques said.

"It like being on the very top of the world," I murmured.

After tea we had to hurry home to get back before curfew.

Next morning we were astonished to see three beehives in the field.

"We need something sweet," Dad said, "the bees may help us survive."

He spent hours reading a book called, "The Inhabitants Of The Apiary And Their Care."

A few days later he went to see how the honey was coming along. He disappeared up the garden, and then we saw him running back pursued by hundreds of bees.

Mum opened the door, and slammed it behind him; even so the kitchen was filled with the sound of humming. I held the living door open, and he and Mum rushed past, and I shut it quickly before the bees could get in.

As we watched his face started to swell. Mum got some tweezers and took out the stings, and then I dabbed the places with vinegar.

Later Jacques came in and we told him what had happened. When we looked at Dad we felt very sorry for him, he looked as if he had mumps, with lots of double chins reaching to his chest.

When Lesley and Muriel saw him they fell about laughing behind his back.

"You're really nasty," Jacques said, "and when we have honey you'll be sorry 'cause we'll make sure you don't get any."

Next Dad arrived home with a hat with fine netting that covered his neck and face, and big gloves that covered his hands.

"Now the bees won't be able to sting me," he said confidently, "and look at this."

He took out something that looked a bit like a gun, "This puffs out smoke, and makes the bees sleepy."

At last the day arrived when the honey was collected. Another beekeeper came to help remove the combs In return for honey he brought a drum that spun around, and we watched with fascination as the golden honey ran out through the tap at the bottom into all the jam jars we'd collected.

After the honey had been extracted there was a pile of wax. Jacques and I took some outside to the hedge, and sat down. We took big lumps of wax and chewed and chewed, and got out the very last drops of honey.

We were wiping our sticky chins when Lesley sauntered past.

"What are you eating? Give me some."

We ignored her, and pretended we hadn't heard.

When we went in Mum was smiling with satisfaction as she looked at the jars of honey in the larder.

"This will help us in the winter," she said, "and there'll be enough to exchange for some winter shoes for you."

It was a few days later when I had my brilliant idea.

"Jacques, let's make some money, then we can buy Christmas presents for everyone. Last Christmas was terrible, because Mum was so ill."

"How?" he asked dubiously.

"We'll collect blackberry leaves to make tea, and in the autumn acorns to grind into coffee."

So we collected baskets of blackberry leaves, and dried them in the sun, then we sold them to anyone who would give us a few pfennigs. Adele, who lived across the road, gave us most, and soon we had quite a few coins.

"Tonight we're going to do something dangerous," Dad told me a few days later " but it's secret, and you can't tell Jacques."

"But Jacques and I tell each other everything," I protested.

"You cannot tell him this," Dad said sternly.

"You know we planted wheat in the field at the back of the vinery, well we're not giving it all to the controlling committee, tonight we are going to take some for ourselves."

After curfew, when it was dark, we left the house and hurried to the field. As we passed Grandmère's house I looked up at Jacques's window, but no one looked out. He'd be so mad, I thought, if he knew what he was missing.

All the places we knew so well seemed strange and mysterious in the darkness.

"We need more twine, Marianne," Dad said, as we were filling the bags, "you must go home to get some."

Passing the greenhouses, the moon's reflection shone on the glass. The moonlight was quite bright, but the shadows were very dark. Reaching the clump of bamboo the leaves whispered. I kept thinking there might be thieves hiding, and my heart seemed to jump.

I crept past Max's house, and then up our path, and the gravel crunched under foot. I tiptoed, and kept standing still, looking around, and listening. It was frightening going into the dark, empty house; there were creaks as if some one was upstairs. I grabbed the ball of twine and ran.

The journey back was just as terrifying. As Dad took the twine he said, "You've been quick." It had seemed an eternity to me.

The next morning when we went to the field there were some of our friends and neighbours waiting, because the authorities had given permission for gleaning. Mum, Grandmère, and the others, including horrible Lesley and her mother, started following the reapers, picking up any grains of wheat that were on the ground. No one noticed that some of the wheat had disappeared.

We all worked in the hot sun, and there were groans and murmurs about pain in the back, but despite that everyone collected little bags of grain.

I was just going to say to Jacques, "I wish it was as cool as last night," then remembered that was a secret.

As we worked the circle of wheat in the middle of the field grew smaller and smaller. The men called their dogs, and picked up big sticks.

We knew that there were rabbits hiding in the wheat. Suddenly one dashed out, and a man with a stick killed it. Then rabbits were running, and dogs were catching them. I wanted to shut my eyes, but didn't, and soon it was all over.

"I'm pleased some of the rabbits escaped," Jacques said, "but glad there were enough for every family to have one."

When we got indoors Mum put the rabbit in the larder for stew next day.

"This has been the best holiday ever," I said, when we were having supper, and Jacques nodded in agreement.

Adonis the bull.

DETESTABLE LESLEY
Chapter 21

The holiday ended and one morning Miss Sanders said, "Get out your reading books, while I mark your work." One good thing about this was that Miss Sanders was busy, and she left us alone. Everyone was absolutely quiet, reading the dullest books imaginable.

As the bell rang for playtime we all sat up straight. Miss Sanders looked at us, "Lift the lids of your desks for inspection."

I groaned, my desk as usual, was untidy.

She walked around the room, and when she looked in a desk said, "Good, you may go."

She came to my desk, and shook me until my teeth rattled.

"As expected, just like a pig's sty. Stay behind, and tidy your desk. As a punishment tidy the book shelves, then you may go."

I tidied up as quickly as possible, and there was time to play. Outside all the class was in the shrubbery arguing.

"No you're wrong," said Lesley, "The doctor brings babies to the house in a black bag."

I knew the truth and said, "I've seen calves being born, and it's the same for humans."

Everyone stared at me, "We start from a tiny seed, and grow in our mother's tummy, and when we're ready we come out."

"How do we come out?" asked Nancy.

"I guess from her tummy button," said Iris.

"No we don't, we come out from an opening between her legs, just like the baby calves."

Everyone looked doubtful.

Just then the bell rang, and we hurried back into the classroom.

Miss Sanders was waiting,

"Reverend Mother has asked me to tell you that next week we're going to have Sports Day."

Everyone looked cheerful; sports day was fun!

Next break we talked about the races.

"Will you be my partner for the three-legged race?" asked Jane,

"Yes, that'll be good, I'll bring some rope, and then we can practice."

Next day Jane and I tied our legs together and set off, and immediately fell over. We tried again, and were soon running really fast.

"I think we'll win this race," said Jane, and I nodded in agreement.

When we went back into the classroom, it was composition. I started writing another boring story. In fact it was so boring that I stopped writing, and looked out of the window. There was someone walking up the drive, it was Lesley's mother. She knocked on the Convent door and went inside.

At the end of the afternoon Reverend Mother walked in. Everyone stood up quickly. She looked around, and walked over to me.

"Here is a letter, make certain you give it to your Mother."

I curtsied, took the letter wondering what was inside.

When Mum read it she sounded puzzled.

"I have to come to the Convent tomorrow, I wonder what they want to talk about."

I was completely baffled, and couldn't think of any reason, but hoped that perhaps my work was improving.

The next afternoon when I came home Mum was sitting in her chair, she looked angry.

"Marianne you've been talking about private things in public. You could have been expelled, that would be a total disgrace."

"I didn't do anything." I was astonished.

"You must have, I heard that you've been saying disgusting things."

"I only told them where babies come from."

"Well one child's mother was very, very angry. She wanted you expelled, but Reverend Mother says she'll give you one chance, so you must behave in future."

"It's that awful Lesley, she is always getting me into trouble."

"Well, you wouldn't have got into trouble, if you'd thought before you opened your mouth."

I shrugged, "Well I'll try," but really I couldn't think what was so wicked.

The next day Reverend Mother sent for me.

She looked sorrowful, "It's sad that a child like you should be so sinful." She went on and on, and I stopped listening, until I heard, "And as a punishment you will stay in the class room when the other well behaved children go out to Sports Day."

Jane was sorry when she heard that I was going to miss one of the best days of the school year, but felt a bit better when Iris agreed to be her partner in the three-legged race.

On the morning of Sports Day everyone helped taking out the equipment. It was a lovely sunny day, not too hot, just the day to have lots of fun.

I hoped that perhaps Reverend Mother would change her mind, but at two o'clock everyone lined up, except me.

Miss Sanders put down pages of sums, and smiled her nasty smile.

"Behave yourself, if that's possible," she ordered, and then led the children out.

As Lesley went through the door, she turned and stuck out her tongue.

I sat alone, feeling really miserable. There was the sound of cheers outside and I felt tearful, and then quickly wiped my eyes; no one must think I minded, and decided to say I didn't want to go to the stupid Sports Day anyway.

I sat in the hot stuffy room wondering whom I hated most, Miss Sanders or Lesley.

CHRISTMAS SURPRISES
Chapter 22

Soon Jacques and I were so busy there was no time to think about school. We had suddenly remembered our plans to earn money to buy Christmas presents. The blackberry leaf money wasn't enough, so we collected acorns, and Mum roasted them in the range, and we ground them up into what people called ersatz coffee.

We thought it tasted horrible, but we sold lots, and by November we had enough pfennigs to buy presents, but decided to wait until the holidays to go shopping.

Before that it was my birthday. Mum said that I could ask the six girls in my class to a party.

"Even Lesley?" I asked.

"Everyone," said Mum, "you can't leave one person out."

I really wanted a party, and Lesley and Muriel hadn't been as nasty recently so I thought it would be fun.

By my birthday the house was beautiful, with paper chains, holly and the little Christmas tree.

On my birthday afternoon the girls arrived. It was a lovely party, there was even a birthday tea, with potato cakes with honey, and a birthday cake made from the wheat we'd ground up in the summer. Everyone liked the honey best.

After tea we played charades, then Dad played the piano while we danced. The party ended with 'murder in the dark'. I loved the suspense, and it was scary wandering all over the house in the darkness, waiting for the murderer to pounce.

After the girls had gone home Jacques came in, and we had another tea, and then a game of darts.

"It's been a lovely day, even nasty Lesley was nice," I said, to Jacques.

But I spoke too soon.

The next day everyone was talking about the party, and saying how much they'd enjoyed it, when suddenly Lesley asked, "Do you have a lavatory?"

I could feel myself going pink, "Of course we do, you just didn't see it."

Lesley stared at me, "Perhaps it's in the garden, poor people have lavatories in the garden. As they don't have bathrooms my mother says that's why they're smelly," and she stared even harder, and wrinkled her nose.

I minded so much about what Lesley had said that I couldn't even tell Jacques. But he must have guessed something was wrong because on the first day of the holiday, as we cycled into town to buy the presents, he grinned.

"Thank goodness you've cheered up," he said.

When we arrived in town all the shops were practically empty, although the shopkeepers had put up red crepe paper. We climbed the narrow twisting paths, and arrived at Trinity Square, and came to the little shop owned by old Mrs. Druet.

We were friends, and not long ago I'd bought books, and Jacques had bought marbles.

Jacques told her he wanted to buy a present for Grandmère, and I explained that I wanted a really special present for my Mother, because last Christmas she'd been so ill she'd almost died.

Mrs. Druet went to a cupboard, rummaged around, and brought out a beautiful china figure of a small, slender woman holding up the hem of her dress to shoulder level, the folds of the skirt reaching her feet, and you could see the shape of her body under the dress.

Mrs. Druet told us that the ornament was 'Art Nouveau.'

I liked those words, Art Nouveau, I didn't know what they meant, but they sounded posh.

We counted my share of the money, and I waited breathlessly.

Mrs. Druet smiled, "Well you are fortunate, you have exactly the right amount of money to buy the ornament."

While I'd had been choosing my present Jacques had been exploring the shop, and he placed two big shells on the counter, one was pink and had spikes, the other was shiny, smooth, golden and brown.

"I'd like these please, but is there enough money?" he asked anxiously.

"Just the right amount," said Mrs. Druet.

"You chose those presents for yourself," I said on the way home.

"No I didn't," retorted Jacques, "Grandmère will like them, she might even ask me to look after them for her."

It had seemed as if Christmas would never come, but at last it was Christmas Eve, and there was a knock on the door. Max came in and gave us some gingerbread biscuits.

" These are for you," he said, giving Mum a bottle of pills, "They are from Dr. Hodeige. They are iron tablets to make your blood strong, and he sends you Christmas greetings."

We sat around the fire eating the biscuits, and drinking blackberry tea.

"There are rumours that Alderney is some kind of terrible prison camp," Dad said as soon as he left. "All the islanders left to go to England at the beginning of the war, and now it's full of slave workers, and their guards."

He was right, because a few weeks later Mum had a letter from the Doctor and he wrote, 'Alderney is a bad place, no doubt what so ever,' and then he told her about all the work he had to do.

But now it was Christmas Eve and I didn't want to think about slave workers so I persuaded them to play cards until bedtime.

I woke up early next morning, and there was a rustle of paper, and the feeling of parcels at the bottom of the bed.

I had lovely presents. A cardigan made from wool that I recognized, it had previously been a jumper belonging to Mam Camp. The elbows had worn out and I'd helped her unravel the wool, and wound it into balls. Best of all there were three second hand books, 'Alice Through The Looking Glass,' 'Just William, and 'Anne Of Green Gables.'

After breakfast I gave Mum her present. She opened it slowly, and smiled with delight as she put the ornament on the mantelpiece

Grandmamma and Grandpa came for dinner. Papa had brought a piece of pork, so we knew that he'd hidden another pig. There was chestnut stuffing; we'd collected the chestnuts in the Convent garden, roast potatoes, parsnips, brussel sprouts and apple sauce. It was a feast!

After dinner Jacques arrived. He said they had rabbit stew for dinner, and Grandmère had really liked his presents. She'd given him a pair of socks.

"There's a present for you Jacques, on the landing," Dad said.

We dashed upstairs. On the landing was a box, and when we opened it there was a real football. It looked as if it had been in a good few matches, but Jacques was so pleased he could hardly speak.

While everyone was having their after dinner nap we went out, and kicked the football. Suddenly Max came out and joined in. I hoped Lesley, and any one else we knew, wouldn't come past on an afternoon stroll, and see us.

After we'd finished playing it was teatime. There were scones and butter, and jam.

After the dishes had been washed Dad put on the fairy lights for a few moments, and then we sat in the firelight.

"I wonder what the New Year will bring," Grandpa said.

Jacques and I wondered too, little did we know that soon the biggest adventure of our whole lives would begin.

THE WILDERNESS
Chapter 23

One afternoon we were amazed to see a tremendously fat nanny goat tethered in the middle of the field. Dad said, "We're looking after her for one of my friends at the Ambulance Station. She's going to have babies, and needs lots of grass to eat, and his garden is quite small.

In return we're going to have some of the milk, so there's going to be extra work. You must be responsible for her, and for the kids, when they're born."

We weren't sure we wanted extra work, but knew we couldn't argue.

We had a good look at her, and she looked hard at us.

Jacques sounded surprised, "Just look at her eyes, they're so strange, she doesn't have round pupils like other animals, hers are like slits, they're vertical."

I nodded, "Perhaps that's why, long ago when people believed in witches, goats were called creatures of the devil, but she doesn't look evil, let's call her Nanny."

Jacques agreed, but we were wrong, she was always in trouble.

She dragged up her stake, and ate all the lettuces in the vegetable patch. Then she pulled down the line and ate a pair of knickers, and half a sheet.

The next day she escaped again, and went next door just as Grandmère was coming out of the lavvy. Nanny put down her head, Grandmère went back inside, and the goat butted the door. Grandmère had to wait until Dad heard her calling for help, and came to her rescue.

Jacques was impressed, "I didn't think anything, or anyone, could frighten Grandmère."

Nanny gave us lots of work. We had to carry buckets of water up to the field, take hay to the shed, and clean it out, and every night she had to be taken in for safety.

For the first time we were spending time in the field. We'd never played there before; it was nearly all grass, which was cut for hay. On the far side was, what Dad called, the wilderness. He told us that although it was part of our garden, nothing useful grew because of the poor soil covering rocks, and it stretched a long way back towards the cliffs.

We had tried to explore, but couldn't get in, because of a mass of prickly gorse, and spiky blackthorn bushes.

One morning when we went into the shed Nanny was standing there, and two baby kids were suckling.

"Look, the babies must have been born in the night," I called to Dad.

We spent the whole morning watching the kids. After a lot of discussion we decided on their names. I chose Nanette, because she looked like a little Nanny. Jacques named the black and white one Skippy, because she was already skipping and dancing about.

It wasn't long before we thought that they should have been called Pest and Nuisance. The whole goat family were always up to mischief. Nanny ate more clothes from the washing line. Skippy somehow managed to get in the house, after coming from the coalhouse, and left black hoof prints on the stairs, and then on the eiderdown in Mum and Dad's room.

"Well at least Nanette hasn't got into mischief," I said, but I spoke too soon.

One afternoon, when the front gate was open, she darted away and ran up the lane. Luckily Max was in his garden, and he ran out and caught her.

"It is fortunate for you it was me who captured her, and not someone else, or she might have been dead meat within the hour."

We thanked him, and took the reluctant Nanette home.

"Enough's enough," said Dad, " it's time for weaning, they're eating grass, and don't drink as much milk."

Now we had more work to do. I milked Nanny, but Jacques had to help by holding her still. The kids had their milk from a bucket. To start with we had to put our fingers in the milk so they could suck, but soon they were drinking on their own.

They didn't like being tied up and being away from Nanny, at first they bleated all the time, and then tried to pull up their stakes.

They seemed to settle down until the day when Jacques was moving Skippy. Suddenly she darted away, the rope trailing behind. She ran towards the hedge at the side of the wilderness. There was a laurel bush we'd never noticed before, and she ran through and disappeared.

"Come on," shouted Jacques, "after her."

We crawled under the green bush, and after scrabbling and wriggling, pushed our way through. To our utter astonishment, after a short distance, there was no gorse, only a few blackthorn bushes, some ancient-looking stunted oak trees, even a few patches of grass, and open spaces where the granite rocks were on the surface.

In front of us was Skippy, she seemed to be waiting. We almost reached her when she darted forward into thicker undergrowth, and as we followed found ourselves in a wood.

We seemed to be following a little path made by animals. Now there was a canopy of leaves above us, and occasionally glimpses of sky. There were long trails of ivy hanging down, covering the ground, and almost tripping us up.

Skippy was only a short distance away, but it was impossible to catch hold of the rope, because every time we came near she ran faster.

Suddenly we found the way blocked. In front of us there seemed to be a wall. We tugged and pulled the ivy away, and sure enough there was a granite wall. We moved along, and turned a corner.

"I think this is a building," Jacques said, and then we saw that behind the ivy was the outline of a door

Skippy had discovered a little spring, and was drinking thirstily. Simultaneously we jumped forward, grabbed her tightly, and then found a strong branch, and tied the rope on firmly.

"Now," said Jacques, "let's explore the building."

Removing the ivy we saw that the door was covered in green moss, but with a push and a heave it creaked open.

We saw a long empty narrow room, with an arched roof. It smelt musty, but the stone walls and floor were dry. At one end was a little grate, which had obviously been used long ago, because it was black with soot.

"It's almost like being in a wood, the light's green," I said.

Jacques nodded, "It's because the window's covered in ivy."

Quickly we ran over and pulled away the ivy. The window was small, there was no glass, but the wall was so thick that no rain could possibly get in.

"This could be really cosy, and no one knows about it," I said.

We looked at one another.

"Are you thinking what I am thinking?" Jacques asked, then added, "This would make a perfect den."

"Exactly!" I agreed.

We went outside, and had a drink from the spring, which bubbled over the stones, and then ran away in a little stream. We went and sat with our backs against the wall, which was warm from the sun.

"What do you think this building is?" wondered Jacques.

"I know," I replied. "Grandpa told me that long ago everyone was afraid that the French army, and their great General Napoleon, were going to invade England and Guernsey.

In just one year all the stonemasons in Guernsey built towers by the beaches, and stone buildings across the island for the soldiers to shelter in, or to store ammunition. I think this is one of those buildings, and perhaps a fisherman used it afterwards. Anyway, no one is using it now, so it's ours."

We got up and carefully pulled the door closed, and holding tightly onto Skippy's rope pushed through undergrowth, and ducked under branches, emerging at last into the field.

It was time to take the goats to the shed for the night. We tied them up, and gave them some hay; and then Dad came and put the enormous padlock on the door.

The next few days we were tremendously busy. First we collected all the things, which would be useful from our den in the bamboo, and the old shed. There was a broom, saucepan, frying pan, two enamel mugs, some plates, a couple of cushions, an old moth-eaten blanket, and a rug that we'd used to use on picnics on the beach.

It was hard work carrying everything, and we had to make certain that no one saw us entering, or leaving, the wilderness.

We worked hard making the den comfortable. First the floor was swept, and then the brush was used to bring down the long cobwebs hanging from the roof. Next we carried in bracken, and made a couch by covering it with the blanket. Last of all everything else was placed on the stone shelf, which was at the side of the grate.

"This is better than a den," I said, "it could be a little house."

"I wonder if a fire would burn in the grate?" pondered Jacques, "then we could bake potatoes. If only we had some matches, but they're impossible to get, Grandmère only has two boxes left, and she doesn't know what we'll do when they've gone."

"I've an idea," I said, "if it works I'll show you tomorrow."

In the afternoon I hurried to Westwood, and running in helped Grandmamma with her dusting. On the mantelpiece there was the flint machine, and I looked at it carefully, because that's what Grandpa used to light the fire.

"How does this work?"

"Well," said Grandmamma, "You can see the metal handles, if you squeeze them together quickly the little wheel turns against the flint, and that makes a spark. It's hard work, but if Grandpa perseveres he can make enough sparks to light the paper in the grate, and start a fire."

Right, now I knew what to do. As soon as the dusting was finished I hurried to the washhouse, which wasn't used because there wasn't enough fuel.

In the corner, behind the big mangle, was a shelf, and sure enough there was the flint machine I remembered seeing. Deciding everyone else had forgotten it was there, and no one was going to miss it, I quickly put it in the carrier on my bike.

When I got home it was late and Jacques was going in, I called out, "Meet you tomorrow at our usual place."

The next morning I took some sheets of newspaper, the fire maker, and when Mum wasn't looking, a small potato from the box under the table and hoped she wouldn't notice.

Jacques was waiting at the den. He was really excited when he discovered how the fire maker worked. We collected some twigs, rolled up the newspaper, and put it in the grate, and tried to make sparks.

At first nothing happened, and our fingers became very sore. Suddenly there was a spark, then more, and the paper caught alight, and we slowly placed sticks on top, taking turns blowing on the flames, until there was a little fire, and we put in the potato.

While it was cooking we went to explore, and when we came back the fire was glowing red and the potato was cooked. While it was cooling we put out the fire with water, and had to jump back because it hissed and spat out ash.

We sat outside and broke the potato in half, the skin was black and sooty, but we ate every bit, the potato was so small we were still starving. Jacques was having dinner with us so we hurried home, and sat down at the table

Mum brought in our plates and we saw we had jacket potatoes, carrots and cheese.

" It's very strange," she said, "I always count the potatoes to make sure we have enough and one has disappeared. It would be too big for a mouse to take, so I hope we haven't got a rat."

"That's not the only strange thing," Dad said, "there was a trail of smoke coming from near the cliffs. No local person would waste fuel so it must be someone up to no good. We must keep our eyes open for anything suspicious."

I sat still with horror, and then glanced at Jacques, he was staring at his plate.

"We have to be far more careful in future," I said when we went outside.

Jacques nodded, "We can only have a fire when it's dark or foggy, and be extra watchful going in and out of the wilderness."

I shivered; it all seemed a bit frightening.

TOMASZ
Chapter 24

It was wonderful having the wilderness and a den of our own, no adults to interfere, we could do exactly as we liked. We were lucky because everyone was so preoccupied with what was happening in the war, and also about finding enough to eat, that they didn't bother much about us; they had too much to think about. So, when we'd finished our tasks, we were free.

One morning I was sitting in one of my favourite hiding places, behind the bush on the bank in front of the cottage. It was a good place to sit, spying on people passing, listening to what they were saying.

There was no one in the road when suddenly there was a rumbling sound, someone shouting, and a murmur of voices that were coming nearer and nearer. Around the corner appeared a line of slave workers, dressed in rags, and worn out tattered shoes.

Some of them were pulling a cart piled high with metal posts, the remainder shuffling along behind. There was a fat soldier swaggering up and down, shouting orders, and pushing the men, trying to make them hurry.

At the end of the line was a tall man as thin and ragged as his companions, but he wasn't, like the others, staring at the ground, or at the man in front, he was looking around.

One of the men tripped and fell; lying on the ground, his face deathly white, and his bones showing under his skin, he almost looked like a skeleton. The tall man walked across and took his arm, lifting him up.

The guard ran over, his face distorted with anger, screaming and punching both men. The tall man didn't let go, he helped the other to his feet, and stood between him and the soldier, so he received most of the kicks and blows. It was difficult to breathe; I was so frightened.

Suddenly there was a loud clatter and crash, a wheel had come off the cart, and everything tumbled onto the ground. No one moved for a moment. Then the soldier became even redder in the face, and ran over, punching any one who got in his way.

He pointed to the men who had been pulling the cart, shaking his fist as they tried to put the wheel on again.

There was movement at the cottage opposite, and Adele was standing in the doorway. I remembered that Grandmamma frequently said that Adele was a brazen hussy, and a collaborator because she went out with German soldiers.

She must have heard the commotion, and stood for a moment looking at what was happening, then she slowly sauntered down, and leaned on the gate. The German guard saw her, he shouted an order, then left the men, walked over, saluted, smiled and they began to talk.

Almost at once the prisoners, who weren't working, moved to the stream, and cupping their hands, began to drink thirstily. Then they slowly walked into the shade of the lane, and lay down.

The tall prisoner came and sat in front of the bush where I was hiding.

"Hello, what is your name?" he whispered.

I gasped with astonishment; no one had ever spied me before.

"Marianne," I replied, edging closer, "What are you called?"

"Tomasz, we come from the camp in the field at the top of the road."

We all knew the camp; it was really an old farm, with outbuildings, and a guardhouse where the soldiers lived. We wanted to explore, but knew there would be terrible trouble if anyone caught us.

I felt very sorry for Tomasz, he was so thin, and his arms and face were cut and bruised.

"Is it true what people say, you're beaten and starved?" I asked.

Tomasz sighed, "Yes it's true, but this is war. We get out at night, and find food in the fields, so we survive."

I was wondering why he could speak English so much better than Max. He seemed to read my thoughts.

"It is so good to speak again in English. It was what I studied in the University in Warsaw, which is in Poland. I was at college when the Germans came, took my country, and brought me here," he said.

Suddenly the soldier blew his whistle, we both jumped, as he angrily shouted orders. The men reluctantly got up, and I whispered quickly, "If I can get any food I will leave it for you behind the gate post."

I wasn't certain that he'd heard as he walked to help reload the cart, then he moved to the end of the line, and the men shuffled off.

The German turned, smiled at Adele who smiled back, and then they both waved.

After they had disappeared around the corner I thought about what Tomasz had said, about going out at night, which meant after curfew. He must be one of the men that everyone fears, I thought. These are the men Papa Camp tries to catch, who milk his cows, and killed his calf. Everyone is frightened, that's why we have big bolts on our doors.

I went to find Jacques, and told him what had happened.

"I'm frightened Tomasz may be dangerous. The slaves killed Scotty and ate him, every day cats and dogs are stolen, he might even eat Tibby Puss. He could even kill us."

"Tell me about Tomasz," said Jacques.

"Well, he wears clothes like a slave worker, but he stands up straight. He's really brave because he helped a man who fell down, and when he did that he was hit by the German guard."

Then I realized that it was silly to be frightened of Tomasz, and said, "He would never hurt anyone."

Jacques nodded in agreement, "We'll help him as much as we can."

First we took some potato peelings, and I hid a carrot from my dinner, and even though Jacques was still very hungry he hid a slice of the saw-dusty bread from his tea. We put the food in an old biscuit tin, and hid it by the gatepost.

Early next morning I ran out, and found that the food had disappeared. A little later there was the sound of the cart, which the workers pulled, coming nearer.

I darted behind the bush. It was clear that Adele must also have heard the same sound because she was walking slowly down her path to the gate.

As soon as the soldier saw Adele he shouted an order, once again the men hurried into the shade.

Tomasz came and sat in front of the bush and whispered, "Thank you."

I told him about Jacques, and how we were going to put food out as often as possible.

He talked about his mother and father, and his little brother.

"I wonder how they are, and if I will ever see them again, because terrible things are happening in Poland." He sounded really sad.

Suddenly the whistle sounded, and the men struggled up slowly, and got into a raggle-taggle line.

The German give Adele a packet. I was certain that it contained food, and wondered why he didn't give some to the starving men.

The next few days we struggled to find scraps to put in the biscuit tin. Usually there were vegetable peelings, and a few slices of the black bread.

One day, when we were walking in the lane, Max called, "Come in, I have for you a treat. It is my birth day, and you must have a biscuit each."

"Oh, thank you," we said together, then, "Happy birthday."

We carried the biscuits carefully to my garden. They were golden brown, and smelled delicious. Jacques licked his finger and put it onto the biscuit, then into his mouth.

"It's so sweet. I can't really remember the taste of biscuits."

I licked my finger and sighed, "Neither can I."

We looked at one another as Jacques said; "We have to give them to Tomasz." I nodded.

The next day was Saturday. I waited, and sure enough there was the sound of the cart, and Adele was waiting at her gate. When the men moved into the shade Tomasz came to the bush.

"Thank you for such a wonderful gift."

I told him about Max. There was silence until Tomasz said, "He is a good German, I had forgotten they could be kind, but they must never be trusted."

Adele and the guard were chatting away and Tomasz said, "I think we will have a long rest to-day. Do you know what is happening in the war?"

"My Grandfather tells me a lot about the war. In Russia the Germans are losing, and being driven back, he thinks it won't be long before the Americans and British soldiers fight on the Continent, and perhaps the war will end."

As the soldier blew his whistle Tomasz said, "I pray that he is right."

The next few days the soldier didn't come past, and we decided that the slave workers had been taken to work somewhere else on the island.

A week later, very late at night I suddenly woke up. There was the sound of running feet, shouts and whistles; jumping out of bed I ran to the window, there were shadowy figures in the road. Suddenly Mum pulled me away from the window as shots rang out.

I went into Mum and Dads' bed because it felt safer.

"I thought it was the British coming to liberate us, but it's probably the Germans trying to catch a thief," Dad said.

In the morning I woke up at six o'clock so curfew had ended. I dressed and crept into the garden. Everything was still, and even though it was early the sun was warm. Tibby Puss was sitting on the step and walked over, rubbing my legs and purring. I walked up the garden towards the apple trees, and decided to have a swing.

As I neared the trees, there was a shape underneath. Was it a shadow?

I paused, what was it? Moving forward cautiously, my heart beating faster, I peered, and saw that there was a person, who wasn't moving, lying on the ground. Creeping nearer saw, to my horror, that it was Tomasz, lying in a pool of blood.

INTO HIDING
Chapter 25

Tomasz was lying on his back, his face as white as chalk, but there was a purple bruise, and on his forehead a deep cut. Was he dead?

I knelt beside him, there was the sound of breathing, and suddenly he gave a groan and opened his eyes. He stared, but didn't seem to recognize me.

" It's me, Marianne, what's happened?"

He tried to smile, and then closed his eyes.

"I hit a German, I may have killed him, but I fought the others and escaped," he whispered.

"What are you going to do?"

He didn't respond, and then groaned.

"Wake up, you must wake up, or they'll catch you," I said holding his hand.

Suddenly it was clear what had to be done. I ran as fast as possible to the pump, and brought back the bucket, and splashed water onto his face.

He opened his eyes, "We're in great danger. You must hide, come with me."

It took all my strength to help him sit up. He had a big cut on the back of his head, much worse than the one on his forehead, and his ankle and foot were terribly swollen.

"Come on, you must come on," I insisted, and tried to help him stand up.

"Put your hand on my shoulder, and lean on me. I'll take you to a safe place."

We moved slowly pushing the bushes aside.

" Bend down," I said, and we moved into the wilderness.

It took a long time to get to the den, but at last we reached the door, pushed it open and he stumbled to the bed, and fell down.

I filled the mug with water from the steam, and put it beside him, then covered him with the blanket.

"I'll be back as quickly as I can," I said.

He opened his eyes, murmured something, then seemed to fall asleep.

I hurried to the kitchen; Mum was by the hay box taking out the porridge. She looked very angry.

"Where have you been you naughty girl? I've been calling you, and Dad searched the garden, now he's gone out to the road looking for you."

Dad came in just as I said, "I'm sorry, I didn't mean to worry you, I was in the top field," which was almost true.

"Well, we were worried after the noise in the night, it may be dangerous to go out, you must promise to stay in the garden."

"I promise," I replied, thinking that the wilderness was really part of our garden.

We'd just finished eating when there was a thunderous knocking at the door. There were two German soldiers.

"Last night a worker escaped," one said, "and we're searching for him. Have you seen him?"

Mum and Dad both said no. I said nothing.

"We search your property." Dad nodded.

They went into every room, opening all the cupboards, then into the garden. I watched them from my bedroom window. They walked up the steps and threw open the door of the lavvy; it was lucky no one was sitting there.

I held my breath as they went into the top field. They looked around, and then walked towards the wilderness. One tried to get in, luckily he didn't see the laurel bushes, and the gorse drove him back.

They returned to the house and said, "If you see him call us, do not go near, he is dangerous, and kills."

After they left I asked if I could go out.

"Yes," Mum replied, "but remember what they said, make sure you keep out of trouble."

Jacques was waiting outside, and we went and sat on the steps.

"Do you know what all the fuss is about?" he asked.

I told him all that had happened, and ended saying, "So you see we have to help him."

We hurried to the wilderness, and went in looking behind us all the time for fear of being followed, and reaching the den cautiously pushed open the door.

Tomasz was lying in exactly the same position, and we couldn't wake him.

"Perhaps he's asleep," I said.

"More likely he's unconscious," said Jacques, "he isn't dead because he's breathing. Let's see where he's injured."

We looked at the cuts and bruises, and at his swollen foot and ankle.

"He must have a cut on his leg," Jacques said, "because there's blood on his trousers."

We carefully pulled away the material from his leg, there was a terrible wound, and the skin was hot to touch, and shiny red.

" I think his leg's poisoned," I said, " Dad says people can get blood poisoning from dirty cuts, and that's very dangerous."

"What can we do?" Jacques looked worried.

That's when I had my brilliant idea.

"I've thought of something, come on."

We covered Tomasz up, and went back to the garden.

"Here are your elevenses," Mum called, and gave us two scrubbed carrots. We went to sit under the apple tree and ate them.

"Those German soldiers wouldn't make good detectives," said

Jacques pointing to the ground, "just look at the stains of blood." Sure enough there was a large reddish, brown mark on the grass.

"So what's your idea?" he asked.

"Max."

"Don't be silly. You're going to Max, and say we have one of your prisoners, who's been injured, and we want you to help."

"Of course not. We'll say we want to talk to him about hospitals."

When we got to the house Max was in the garden.

I smiled, "Can you help us? When we grow up Jacques is going to be a doctor, and I'm going to be a nurse, so we're interested in hospitals, but we need some things, and to know what we should do to help ill people."

Max laughed, "Hard work it is, I will help if possible."

"Well, we are going to make pills with mud, and medicine from leaves, but we haven't any bottles. We're going to pretend that we've got coughs, and cuts, and broken bones, but we don't know how to treat them."

"Ah, for the coughs give them cough medicine. Now cuts have to be washed, very clean. Broken bones have to be put in a splint, but if not broken may be a sprain, cold water very good, and leg or arm must rest.

Now you want things I can give?"

"Yes please," we said.

Max led the way into the surgery.

"Here is a little box for pills. We do not have many bandages, but we have some made of paper, not very good, but one for you, and two bottles."

I noticed that one bottle had been washed, but in the other there was some brown liquid. Max noticed me looking and said, "A little iodine left, very good to stop badness coming."

I remembered when I fell over how much iodine hurt, and Dad said that it prevented blood poisoning.

"Have good game," Max said as we thanked him

We hid the things in the garden, and agreed to meet after dinner. When we finished eating I went to the cupboard where Mum stored clean rags, and chose the softest.

We met and went into the wilderness, it was hot and uncomfortable, and the flies were buzzing around us as we walked more and more slowly to the den.

"I'm a bit scared of what we might find," I said, and Jacques nodded.

Slowly we pushed open the door and peered in. Tomasz hadn't moved but his breathing seemed louder.

"Max said that you have to wash wounds clean," Jacques said.

So we filled a bowl with water, and I took a clean rag and gently started washing the cuts on his head.

Tomasz didn't stir, "I don't like looking at this, I don't think I want to be a nurse any more."

The cuts didn't look as terrible when the blood had been washed away. Then we looked at his foot and leg, which were terribly swollen, and we decided not put on a splint because we didn't know where to put it.

"Let's put on a cold, cold rag by dipping it in the spring, because that is what Max told us to do, and Grandmère did that when I sprained my wrist, and that made it better," said Jacques.

Now it was time to deal with the terrible wound on his leg, and this time we both did the washing. It took a long time to get out all the gravel and dirt. Tomasz didn't stir.

"It probably needs stitching up, but we can't do that," I said. "We must put the iodine on." As there wasn't very much I added a little water and shook the bottle, then very carefully poured the iodine into the wound.

The bleeding started again, and we put on the bandage, and sighed with relief as the blood stopped.

Tomasz gave a loud groan, tried to sit up and then fell back, he moved restlessly, and then became quiet, and seemed to have fallen asleep.

We knew we couldn't come back until morning, and Jacques took out a boiled potato and put it by the mug.

"Grandmère didn't see me put it in my pocket at dinner time, she only said, 'do not gulp your food.'"

We shut the door, and placed a stone to stop it blowing open, and went home.

At teatime there was a thud on the mat, it was the Press. Dad came in and put it on the table.

I picked it up and read the headlines:

ESCAPE OF DANGEROUS PRISONER
TOMASZ SIRKOSKY IS VIOLENT AND HAS COMMITTED
CRIMES AGAINST THE THIRD REICH AND CAUSED
INJURIES TO MEMBERS OF WERMACHT.

ANYONE FOUND SHELTERING THIS CRIMINAL WILL BE
SHOT.

BY ORDER OF THE COMMANDANT
2nd OF JUNE 1944.

I didn't want any more tea after that, and went into the garden and stood by the front gate.

Jacques joined me.

"Have you read the Press?" I asked. "They wouldn't shoot children, would they?"

JUNE SIXTH 1944
Chapter 26

T he next morning we walked slowly through the wilderness, scared of what we might find. As we pushed open the door of the den it was wonderful to hear a feeble "hello."

Tomasz was still very white, but he was slowly eating the potato we'd left yesterday.

He smiled, "I thank you with all my heart. I am getting better, and am fortunate to be alive."

"Can you tell us what happened?" I asked.

He nodded, and we sat down and had to listen hard, his voice was not much louder than a whisper.

"You know that most of the slave workers were taken away from the island because the great defences have been built, only a few of us remain. We were so hungry my friend went to see what he could find to eat in the dustbin. Kurt, the German you have seen who guards us, came out and picked up a spade and hit my friend on the head.

I was angry, and ran over, grasped the spade and hit Kurt, cutting his head. He fell to the ground. Perhaps I even killed him.

The other guard came with a big curved knife and hit my head. I ran, and he shot me, and I limped and hid in your garden. All night I could hear them searching."

"We'll look after you," I said. "You must keep your wounds clean, so we'll get some water."

I picked up the bowl, and Jacques followed carrying the bucket.

"He doesn't need a bucket of water silly."

"He can't go to the lavvy, or out in the bushes, and he hasn't got a po so he has to use the bucket," replied Jacques as he threw the contents on to the ground. "I'm not the one who's silly, you are."

We went back, and washed the cuts on Tomasz's head, then he

struggled to sit up, and took the bandage off his leg. He took the rag and cleaned the wound, it still looked terrible, but the redness had gone.

"I was so fortunate. Do you see the bullet went in one side and out the other, and it missed the bone," and he put the bandage on again.

Then he looked at his ankle and foot. "I fell down a bank, I don't think my ankle is broken, but possibly the bones in my feet are damaged, so I cannot walk for a while.

Can I stay here? I know it of dangerous for your family."

"You must stay here, and we'll try and get some food," I said.

"I've got something for you to eat now," said Jacques proudly, "it's cold porridge. We had it for breakfast, and I put some of mine in this jar."

The porridge didn't look very appetizing, but Tomasz ate it all, then looking exhausted pulled up the blanket, and fell asleep.

We crept out, and walked in silence, wondering how we were going to feed him when we hadn't enough food for ourselves.

Dad was waiting, "Come on you two, we're going to the farm. I'm going to help Papa strengthen the stable doors to stop thieves."

As we cycled there were glimpses of the sea, and the cliffs, which were mined. In the fields nearby were tall wooden poles, with wires attached from one to the other.

I was puzzled, "Why have the Germans put up those wires?"

"There are mines at the top of each post," explained Dad, "the Germans think that the British may come to liberate us, and if parachutists land on the wires the mines will explode, and that will be certain death."

When we arrived at the farm there was the smell of dinner cooking, and we each had a plate of boiled onions

"Those mines on posts are so dangerous," Papa grumbled," it makes haymaking very difficult. You mark my words, some one will load their cart too high, and there'll be a terrible accident."

After dinner the adults got on with their work while we searched for eggs. There were only two hens, who roamed in the garden to find food in the day, and were locked in the stable at night.

We found three eggs, and I wrapped one in hay and put it in my saddlebag.

We had lettuce and scones for tea. When no one was looking I put my scone in my pocket.

Mam looked at my plate in surprise, "You must savour your food, not gullop it." Then she looked at Jacques, "You're as bad."

His plate was empty!

When we got home. I looked in my saddlebag, and breathed a sigh of relief because the egg wasn't broken. We put the food in a little basket, and carried it, with the glasses of milk Mum had given us, carefully into the wilderness.

Reaching the den we were amazed to see Tomasz sitting outside.

He grinned, "I was able to crawl out, and it's good to sit in the sun."

I took the food out of the basket, and went to get the flint fire lighter, " Here are a few things to eat. We'll show you how to use the flint, and you can boil the egg, but you must wait until dark so that no one sees the smoke"

Tomasz smiled, "I know about flints, but there's no need, if you get me a mug and fork that would be good."

When he had the mug and fork we watched in amazement as he broke the egg into the mug, beat it with the fork, added the milk, beat them together, and in one gulp drank the lot."

"Urhh," we said simultaneously.

"It is very good," said Tomasz, "you should try." We both shook our heads.

The sun was going down as we helped him back to his bed.

In the night there was the roar of gunfire, and the sound of exploding bombs, and the rattle of anti- aircraft fire, and we all hid under the stairs. We never got used to air raids, they just seemed to get scarier. This raid went on for ages, and it was dawn when it stopped, and we went to bed.

In the morning Mum said, " We had such a disturbed night you can stay home from school."

That was good news, and after breakfast I ran outside and searched the garden looking for shrapnel for my collection, and met Jacques who was also searching. When he heard I was staying home he looked cross, "Grandmère says I have to go, but try to find some food for Tomasz, and meet at the den after school."

I waved goodbye, and hurried to the vinery. I saw that the key was in the door of the greenhouse where peas were growing. The peas were ripe, we had them for dinner every day, and Mum chopped up the pods into a salad for tea. Sometimes it seemed possible we might all turn green we ate so many.

Here was the chance. Quick as a flash I went in, and started picking. I didn't have anything to put the peas in so they went in my knickers, which were big and baggy, and fortunately the elastic was strong.

After it was impossible to get another one in I looked carefully around, and crept out, and walked slowly, as I reached my front gate Lesley suddenly appeared, so she hadn't gone to school either.

"Cor, you look fat," she said.

"I'm not, I've just got on an old dress of Mum's, and it's got a full skirt." I hurried out of sight as fast as I could, and I put the peas in a box, and hid it under a bush.

After dinner Dad and I cycled to Westwood. There were lots of German trucks on the roads carrying soldiers, some of them were wearing helmets, and carrying guns.

As we reached Westwood Dad said, "I'm certain something's up. The Germans have been moving all around the island during the last few days, and Max has been very busy sorting out his medical supplies."

Grandpa was standing at the front window looking at all the traffic. He seemed excited, "Something is happening, the Allies must be going to fight the Germans in France, and perhaps they'll come to the islands as well, and free us."

Dad nodded, "If the English do invade life won't be easy, because we've no where to shelter if there's fighting.

"Then we'll all be killed," Grandmamma looked frightened.

That sounded really scary, what could we do? Perhaps we could all hide in the den.

They carried on discussing what we should do; I saw my chance and slipped out of the room. What could be found that would be useful to Tomasz?

In the cupboard in the greenhouse I found a ball of string, some scissors and even better, a very big penknife, and I hid them in my saddlebag.

In the dining room everyone was still talking about the war, but there was now a teapot with blackberry leaf tea on the table, and some biscuits made with oats.

"This is as good as a birthday tea," I said, wishing it could be shared, even though there wasn't very much, with Mum, Jacques and Tomasz.

That evening when I reached the den Jacques was already there. He'd brought two carrots, and a slice of the saw-dusty bread; he stared in astonishment at the box of peas.

Tomasz was pleased with the food and string, but really excited by the knife. He opened the blades, there were three, and one was very large.

"Good and sharp," he grinned, "don't touch, it could take off your finger."

All that night there was the sound of English planes in the distance, but there was no bombing.

In the morning Dad came back from ambulance duty.

"Something is definitely happening, the Germans are wearing battle dress, with twigs and leaves in their helmets as camouflage,' he said.

He took the crystal set from the hiding place, tickled the crystal with the cat's whisker. We all waited in suspense, and he suddenly shouted, "The invasion of Europe has begun."

Everyone seemed excited and frightened at the same time. We couldn't get any news about the grandparents because the Germans cut off the telephone.

At last the Press was delivered and we read:

INVASION BEGINS AT 5.30 THIS MORNING
Germany will fight with her whole might.
Berlin 10.30 a.m. 6 June 1944

"Well it's official," said Dad, "now we'll have to wait to see what will happen next."

He carried on reading, and the best news, I thought, was that all schools would be closed until further notice.

There was a knock at the door and Jacques and I hurried to the wilderness. Tomasz listened intently as we told him the news that the English and Americans were fighting in France, and that everyone was waiting to see if the British soldiers would come to fight in Guernsey, and liberate us.

"At last, at last," said Tomasz, "perhaps I will see my family again after all."

A GOOD DISGUISE
Chapter 27

Jacques and I were excited, we thought the British soldiers would arrive at any minute, and then ships would come from England bringing back the people who had been evacuated, and best of all, food.

We knew the British soldiers weren't far away fighting in France, because all day and night there was a sound like the rumble of thunder, which never stopped. Dad told us that was the sound of guns, and when he was out at night, with the ambulance, he said that in the distance the sky was red from flames, and there were flashes of gunfire.

Then the sounds of fighting stopped, and Dad listened incessantly to the crystal set.

"It's quite clear," he said a few days later, "no one is coming to liberate us, the soldiers are much too busy driving the Germans back towards Germany. We'll have to wait until Hitler's beaten, then we'll be free."

Mum looked worried, "No boats are coming from France, there's no food, nor coal, or any of the things we need to survive, and nothing either for the Germans."

Dad gave her a hug, "Don't worry, the war can't last much longer, we'll manage."

Tomasz was even more worried than Mum.

"It may be a long time before the British come," he said, "I can't stay here forever, but to leave the Wilderness it is necessary to have clothes, not rags; if I'm seen like this I will be caught immediately, and shot."

"He is getting better," I said to Jacques, "soon he will have to leave the den, but how can we find clothes for him?"

Jacques shook his head. "We'll think if something, but first we must get some food, he had nothing to eat yesterday, and the day before it was vegetable peelings."

We decided to go to Max, to see if we could find anything for Tomasz.

We knocked on the door; when Max came I said, "We're having a picnic and wondered if we can look in your garden for something to eat."

"Yes, yes," he replied, "and I also will look in house."

Although we searched everywhere we only found eight strawberries. When we went back Max was waiting.

"It is good, you will enjoy I think," he said, giving us a parcel.

When we opened the parcel we couldn't believe our eyes; inside there was a fat, German sausage. I knew it tasted delicious because Max had once given me a slice; and even better it didn't need cooking, and lasted for months. There was also a whole black rye loaf of bread.

We stared at one another in amazement.

"It's too much for a picnic," said Jacques, "and he's never given us much food before, he hasn't enough for himself, the Germans are nearly as hungry as us. Perhaps you were right and he suspects we're sheltering Tomasz."

I was puzzled, "It is strange, if Max has anything to share he always gives it to Mum, and then comes to supper. He'd never give us all this for a picnic."

We sat in the warm sun, looking at the food, wondering what Max knew.

" Well," I said, "Tomasz has some real food instead of scraps, and we deserve the strawberries for all our hard work."

As we finished eating Jacques suddenly jumped up.

"I have it! I have it! I know where we can find Tomasz some new clothes."

I was amazed, "How? No one can get clothes, except for second hand stuff in the 'For Sale' or 'Exchange' columns in the Press."

Jacques grinned, "My Grandpère was a Guernsey man, and he met Grandmère in France in the Great War, and married her. He died before I was born. Grandmère was so sad that she kept all his clothes in the spare room, so it seems he has not really gone. We can take some things for Tomasz to wear."

"Don't be stupid," I interrupted," she'll know things have been stolen, and telephone the police, and they might even discover the den."

Jacques was scornful, "I'm not stupid, she dusts the room every week, but she only looks at the clothes when she spring-cleans, so she won't know anything has gone until next year.

Tomorrow, when she goes to town, we'll take what Tomasz needs."

I shivered with apprehension, then nodded, "Well, there's nothing else we can do, just let's hope we don't get caught."

That afternoon, after we'd finished all our tasks, we   went into the wilderness to give Tomasz the food.

His eyes opened wide with astonishment when he opened the parcel.
"Where did this come from?"

"Max."

"Who is Max?"

"We told you about him when he gave us the biscuits, he's our good German friend."

"No German is good. They are all enemies, it may be a trap," said Tomasz fiercely.

"Max is good and kind," insisted Jacques, "he wouldn't hurt anyone."

Tomasz shrugged angrily, but he didn't give the food back, just put it on the shelf.

When we left we noticed that he had opened his penknife, so the sharp blade was out, ready to use at a moment's notice.

The next day I waited until Mrs. Le Marquand set off to town, in fact, I followed her a little way up the road to make certain she'd really gone.

When I tapped on Jacques's back door he opened it cautiously.

"Come in," he whispered, even though there was no one at home I crept in. Mrs. Le Marquand didn't like visitors and I'd never been further than the kitchen. We went into the hall, which was dark and gloomy, and the stairs creaked as we tiptoed up.

Jacques opened a door at the top of the stairs. Inside was a room with a big cupboard, a chest of drawers, a bed, a washstand with a towel all ready to use, a dressing table, set out with a hairbrush and comb.

There was also a photograph of a very smart soldier

"He's my Grandpère," said Jacques, "I'll show you his medals. He was a very brave soldier, but he died young because of his many injuries."

He opened a drawer, there on velvet material, was a long row of medals. He opened another drawer and took out a flannel shirt, a navy Guernsey fisherman's jumper, socks, and some long underpants.

Suddenly we heard the creak of the front gate, we froze, and listened as footsteps walked up the path, then there was the rattle of the letterbox. We both sighed with relief realizing it was the postman.

Quickly Jacques opened the wardrobe, and lifted out some boots from the bottom, and reaching up took down a fisherman's cap.

We carried the things to the kitchen, and went back upstairs to make certain all the drawers and doors were shut. I felt uncomfortable, it really seemed as if Jacques's Grandpère was staring at me.

"Don't worry" whispered Jacques, "he was a Guernsey man and a soldier, he would want to help any one in trouble."

We went back down stairs and stared at the pile of things on the floor, wondering how to get them next door. Suddenly I knew what to do, and whispered, "Stay here, I will be back," and returned pushing the dolls' pram.

We placed all the clothes on the bottom, and put Elizabeth Anne the doll on the top. The back door was firmly shut, and we wheeled the pram back.

Tomasz was astounded when he saw what we'd brought. He put a boot on his good foot, it was a bit big but he said, " I'll put some hay inside the shoes and lace them up tightly, and then they'll fit.

Next he put on the trousers, and tied string around the waist so they didn't fall down, and put on the Guernsey, and had to roll up the sleeves.

"Your Grandfather and I must almost be the same size, he was just a bit bigger."

Next he put on the cap, "Now I am a real Guernsey man."

We looked at him critically.

I laughed, "We'll have to get some scissors first so we can cut your hair and beard, because now you look like Robinson Crusoe."

As we were going home I asked, "Why did we whisper when we were in your house?"

"I think it was because we were frightened we'd be caught, I have never been so scared in all my life," replied Jacques.

HARD TIMES
Chapter 28

The next morning we hurried to the wilderness, and we hesitated for a moment when we saw a figure, and then walked cautiously forward and stared in amazement. It was Tomasz, but Tomasz as we'd never seen him. He had managed to cut his hair and trimmed his beard. He looked like a Guernsey fisherman.

"You certainly no longer look like a slave worker," Jacques said.

"I am no longer a slave. I am free and will remain so for ever," Tomasz spoke decisively. "You do not need to bring me food. I can now walk quite well. I would like to carry on using this building, but you must not worry if I am not here when you come."

I felt very worried, "It will be difficult finding food. No boats come from France now the Germans are being driven back. Everything we had from France is being used up. There is hardly any coal left, nothing for the doctors and the hospital, there's no food, every one is nearly starving. Even the Germans are hungry. Papa Camp saw some searching in his dustbin for something to eat."

"Do not worry," said Tomasz, "when I was a boy I spent the summers with my Grandfather in the forest. I know which plants and fungi to eat, and I hunt with this."

We stared as he took out what looked like a strip of rubber, joined to a forked stick.

"It is a catapult. I have kept it hidden from the Germans when I was their prisoner. It works like this."

He picked up a round stone from a pile near the door, put it in the pouch, pulled back it far back, and said, "I will hit the trunk of that tree."

He stood, took aim, the stone flew through the air and hit the tree with a loud thwack.

"I have used it already, look inside." We looked in the den, and saw a rabbit hanging from the hook.

Then I remembered seeing feathers drifting in the wind and asked, "Have you used it to kill birds?"

Tomasz nodded.

"Not song birds like blackbirds?"

He nodded again, "When you starve you kill anything, but I try to kill pigeons, they have more meat."

We were thankful not to have to find food for Tomasz, but now I had another big problem. School was going to reopen, and I'd grown out of my school sandals, and no matter how hard I pushed my feet in they were too uncomfortable to wear for any length of time, in any case they were completely worn out, there were even holes in both the soles.

During the holidays Jacques and I had mostly gone bare foot, and on visits to the farm we had put on our wellingtons. When I had gone to town, or to Westwood, I'd squashed my feet into the sandals.

Mum searched the 'Exchange' and 'For Sale Column' in the Press, just as she had before. One day when I went in there were some tatty old plimsolls, and a pair of boy's shoes, that weren't too worn, on the table, but when I tried them on were at least two sizes too big.

"I can't wear those," I protested, "they are horrible, clumpy and heavy, they are much too big."

"Perhaps your feet will grow by the winter," Mum said, "we can put an inner sock into each shoe. We will have to see when the time comes; anyway you can wear the plimsolls now. We even have some whitener so you can keep them clean."

"They are not school uniform, Reverenced Mother will send me home," I wailed.

Mum spoke firmly, "I will write a note, there is nothing else I can do."

On the first day of term I walked slowly to school, clutching the note. Looking around the playground there was no one else wearing plimsolls; they were wearing shoes or sandals, even if they were a bit shabby.

Lesley sauntered over; she was wearing smart brown sandals, and I guessed that they'd come from the black market.

"What have you got on your feet? Those plimsolls, if you can call them plimsolls, they look really silly, especially with your black tablier. I guess you are going to be told off."

The bell rang and we went to the classroom. Miss Sanders was waiting. She caught hold of my shoulder, pulled me around and contemptuously looked at my feet. The room became very quiet. "Well, well we have someone who looks as if she is going to play tennis.

Have you brought the tennis balls and a racket?"

Every one laughed, pleased that it they weren't being picked on. I shook my head, and at that moment the door opened, and in walked Reverend Mother.

All the children stood up, I quickly curtsied, and held out the letter. Reverend Mother opened it, sighed and said, "I know it is very difficult to get school uniform, ask your parents to do their best, but if it is difficult we understand."

At playtime my friends agreed that Miss Sanders and Lesley were as nasty as one another, and as we chatted I thought that there were times when school was really good.

On the way home Lesley and her friend walked behind me. They kept laughing and calling out, "Who's got white shoes? Marianne's got white shoes. Who thinks she can play tennis? Marianne couldn't hit a ball if she tried."

Reaching home I turned round, "Why don't you grow up, and stop being so stupid," and then ran in before they could respond.

Mum was dishing up dinner and looked up. "It wasn't as bad as you feared was it?" she asked. I shook her head; it was impossible to say what had really happened, Mum had so many things to worry about.

LET'S GO FISHING
Chapter 29

Life was much easier when we didn't have to find food for Tomasz, however we still usually went to the den every day. Frequently he was there, and would tell us stories about the days he had spent with his Grandfather in the big forests in Poland. He never told us where he went on the days he spent away from the den. If we asked he would reply, "Better you don't know."

We were often hungry, most of our meals were made from vegetables, and sometimes there was a little ration of meat. One morning Mum called out, "Just see what Tibby Puss has brought home." There, on the doorstep, was a dead baby rabbit. Mum gave him the head to eat while we had delicious rabbit stew.

"He must know we are hungry, and he is feeding us," I said. Mum agreed, but Dad shook his head, " Cats always bring home their prey, and it has nothing to do with the needs of humans."

Anyway we were all very thankful that now and again another rabbit appeared on the doorstep, but we weren't keen on the mice! I couldn't imagine eating mice or rats, but we knew that's what the slave workers used to eat when they had nothing.

Occasionally Max would turn up around suppertime, and we always shared what we had with him. Poor Max used to be plump; well to be honest, very fat, now he was scrawny. He always hesitated a moment before tucking in greedily.

One evening he said, "It is hard for me, many soldiers are ill, so I have much work all over the island. Please God this war ends soon, I fear much for my family."

When he went Mum said, "Now we know why we don't see him very often, I think he's away working nearly all the time."

One morning Dad and I were in the garden when a group of men in

153

tattered uniforms, guarded by a German soldier, walked up our path, climbed over the hedge into the fields beyond.

"I thought the slave workers had gone,"

"I don't think they're slave workers," said Dad. "They're probably Russian soldiers who were forced to join the German army. Now the Russians are defeating the Germans in great battles the soldiers on the island don't trust them any more.

They must be taking a short cut to Saint's harbour to work on the fortifications, but what a cheek to come through our garden."

I was just relieved that they didn't go into the wilderness, and Mum was sorry for them, and put out vegetable peelings that they stuffed into their mouths.

The men ignored me, but one evening there was a knock at the door, when we opened it there was the guard.

He smiled, and held out a slice of black bread to me, and said, "For kinder," and put it into my hand.

I knew kinder meant child, but couldn't believe that someone, who must be very hungry, could be so generous.

Dad invited him in; and I greedily ate the black bread remembering how once I'd hated the taste, and now was pleased to eat every crumb.

The German didn't speak very much English, but we found out that he was called Huburt Schulz.

Every evening he turned up bringing his bread ration for me. He showed us photographs of his mother, father and sisters. He gave me a photograph of himself looking very smart in what must have been his new uniform.

Soon he knew lots of English words, and I taught him how to play snap.

One evening he didn't come until it was almost bedtime, and then there was the familiar knock.

Huburt was standing there and said to Dad, "Come, we fish," Dad seemed puzzled, but followed him.

Mum looked scared, "Where can they be going? The nearest place is Saint's harbour, but all the land near the coast is mined, and we know from the Press that people have been blown up, and killed in the minefields."

We waited, an hour passed, and then another, it was after curfew and getting really dark when there were footsteps, and Huburt and Dad walked in. They were carrying a big sack, which they opened. Suddenly there were fish, most were dead, a few alive, flopping and slithering everywhere. Some were in the basin, some on the table, and some on the floor, which was splattered with blood.

Huburt put some of the fish back in the sack, while Mum built up the fire, got out the frying pan and cooked. We sat down and ate. It was the most delicious food I could remember, and also the first midnight feast I'd ever eaten.

After we had finished Huburt went off with the sack of fish for his friends, and I went to bed.

When I got up Mum had cleaned the rest of the fish, boiled up the fish heads and bones, and made a delicious soup.

When we were having dinner, and Tibby Puss was eating some of the bits, Dad told us what had happened the night before.

"We set off towards the cliffs and came to signs that say 'ACHTUNG MINEN.' Huburt said, "Follow carefully."

We started making our way down a little twisting path towards the harbour; we crept along, talking in whispers. The hairs on the back of my neck stood on end, and my hands were clammy, it was so frightening. We passed a gun emplacement, and my heart started to pound, but we weren't challenged.

When we reached the harbour it was fortified with concrete bunkers, but again no one appeared. Now I was even more worried, if we weren't blown up I could be shot for being in a restricted zone.

On the slipway, was a rackety, old, rowing boat, it seemed very strange because we had no fishing tackle. We pushed it in the water. Huburt rowed, and I bailed out with a tin can because a lot of water was coming in.

There still didn't appear to be any fishing lines or bait, and as it was now dusk there didn't seem to be much chance of success.

To my astonishment, when we reached the middle of the bay, Huburt took out a hand grenade, pulled out the pin and threw it into the sea. There was a muffled boom, and the water surged up. The surface of the water was covered with fish, and the water was pink with blood.

While we were collecting the fish the water was still coming into the boat, and the load became so heavy it seemed likely that we would sink. However, at last we reached shore safely.

After the grenade exploded I expected someone on the cliffs to fire, or to see hoards of Germans rushing down, but nothing happened.

The journey back up the cliff was horrific. The sack was dripping wet, the fish were heavy, and it was getting dark so it was very difficult to see the path, and I was terrified we might stand on a mine.

It's good to have the fish but I really hope Huburt doesn't invite me to go fishing again."

For the rest of the day Jacques and I were busy giving fish to Grandmère, and taking some to the farm and to Westwood.

Grandmamma was very suspicious, so I said Dad had got the fish from a friend. Well that was true, but I wondered if she would still have eaten it if she'd known that it came from a German.

It was the end of the afternoon by the time we finished helping with the fish, and we felt happy as we walked to the den knowing we had enough for dinner for the next three days.

When we arrived Tomasz was outside sharpening his knife, He didn't say anything, just scowled. I was surprised because he was always pleased to see us.

Suddenly he growled, "There was a German in your home last night, and your Father had been out with him, they were carrying a sack.

I told him about Hubert, and the fish, and said we were sorry we couldn't bring any fish to him.

He looked even angrier, "It is a trap, we will all suffer, even when you are hungry you do not take terrible risks. Your parents must like Germans, their enemies, there is another soldier that goes to your house."

"Yes, that's Max, who sent the sausage you ate."

Tomasz scowled even more, "I go now to look for food," and he stumped off into the bushes.

We walked slowly home.

"He didn't even say good-bye," said Jacques.

"No he didn't, and he must spend time spying on Mum and Dad and me. I thought he was our friend, and trusted us."

Saints Bay where Dad and Huburt went fishing. Note the tank traps.

Huburt Anton Schulz who helped Marianne's family

TIBBY PUSS IS LOST
Chapter 30

We didn't see Tomasz for a few days, then he returned and seemed as friendly as ever. He didn't ask about Huburt, but he needn't have worried because he'd been moved to another part of the island.

We were all very busy, trying to find food for the long winter months.

"If only we still had the bees," I said, "no one knew why they'd died in the spring."

"Well we mustn't grumble," Mum said, "we are so fortunate to have the vinery." But she spoke too soon.

We were just eating dinner when an official-looking letter fell on the mat

"Oh no!" Dad said as he tore it open. "The Germans are taking over the vinery to produce food for their troops. Now what are we going to do?"

We sat in silence, Mum looked as if she might cry.

Dad smiled reassuringly, "Don't worry, it'll be all right. Reg Blanchford keeps asking me to work full time for the Ambulance Service, so we'll have some money to buy anything that's available. We have vegetables planted in the field by the wilderness; and they are hidden behind bushes so they shouldn't get stolen, and there's always the farm.

Now we must get as much as possible from the vinery to-day, but it'll be difficult because no one must know what we're doing."

I made journey after journey carrying vegetables in the doll's pram, and Jacques carried the wood Dad managed to cut down from the hedges.

By evening we had two sacks of potatoes hidden under the bed, carrots buried in sand in a tub so they would keep, two big bags of dried haricot beans, and one bag of butter beans hidden in the wardrobe, and four boxes of big, fat, Spanish onions.

In the cupboard was a little bag of sugar Mum had bought on the black market, a bag of flour, and five jars of black, sugar beet treacle. At the back of the washhouse was a pile of wood.

That night we sat around the table at supper, quite exhausted, knowing we didn't have very much but we were luckier than other people.

Dad was busy next day. The goats had gone long ago, and there was hammering and banging in the shed that had been Nanny's shelter.

When we went in there were five rabbit hutches. The next day each hutch was occupied. There were three small grey rabbits, one white, and one black.

They were sitting on beds of sweet-smelling hay that Dad had brought back from the farm. There was also a new, extremely large, padlock on the door.

We called the grey rabbits Smokey, Snuffles and Misty, the white one Snowball, and my favourite, the black rabbit, Blackberry.

When we told Dad he frowned, "Just remember these are not pets, we're keeping them for food."

When we'd eaten our tea Dad told us how he'd got the rabbits. He'd taken some potatoes, some beans, and a jar of treacle to exchange, but had also given a great deal of money.

He frowned, "I could have bought a really expensive bike before the war with the money I spent on those rabbits."

The next day Dad began working for St. John's Ambulance. Some times he worked in the day, often all night. When he came home we always wanted to know what he'd been doing.

"Well," he said, "it's a funny old job, now there's hardly any petrol we have problems. We tried burning charcoal to drive the engine and that was all right, but it's hard to get charcoal, so now we have a horse, and an ambulance made out of a removal van. There's a man who is in charge of the horse, and he drives the van. We do have the real ambulance for emergencies."

Every day we felt hungrier and hungrier, and there wasn't much food for Tibby Puss, only an occasional saucer of milk, but he seemed to manage, and often stayed out all night hunting.

One morning he didn't come running when I called. When I came back from school, and went into the kitchen Mum just shook her head.

Jacques and I ran to the vinery, which wasn't ours any more, and asked the men if we could search for my cat.

The foreman unlocked the greenhouses and sheds. We searched everywhere, Jacques even climbed into the old boiler pit, but Tibs wasn't in the boiler.

We went to Max, and he searched the house, while we looked in the shed, but there was no trace.

This was terrible. Ever since Scotty had disappeared I worried about Tibs, and the notices about the lost animals in the Press had made it worse.

That night Jacques and I wrote out notices "LOST ONE SPECIAL TABBY CAT CALLED TIBBY PUSS. PLEASE LOOK IN SHEDS IF FOUND BRING BACK TO MOULIN HUET COTTAGE. REWARD.

Early next morning we took the notices to every house in the lane, but it was clear that Tibs had disappeared.

The next morning was Saturday; we went to search in the wilderness, calling softly all the time but there was no answering mew.

We went in to the den, Tomasz wasn't around, but in the corner was a pile of, what looked like, rabbit skins. I was frightened to look closely in case they weren't rabbit.

"Jacques you don't think Tomasz would"

He knew what I was going to say and became red in the face.

"How can you even think that?"

"Well, he did say you eat anything if you're really hungry, he must be nearly starving,"

"I know," said Jacques emphatically, "that Tomasz would never do anything to make us unhappy."

Tomasz didn't return, and we stumped out through the wood, with Jacques refusing to talk.

The next morning, when Jacques went to church with Grandmère, I went back in to the wilderness. There was the smell of smoke so Tomasz must have cooked something in the night.

Pushing open the door my eyes became accustomed to the gloom, and there was Tomasz, sitting on the bed, holding something in his arms.

"Is this Tibby Puss?" he asked. "I found him by the cliff. Some one had put down a gin trap to catch a rabbit. Their neck gets caught in a wire and that kills them, but his leg was caught, I heard him crying. He's a good cat; he didn't even scratch me when I freed him. He has cut his leg. I have washed it, but it hurts him to move so he should stay indoors until it is healed."

"I can never thank you enough," I said throwing my arms around Tomasz.

"I can say the same to you," he replied.

I walked carefully back home and saw Jacques in his garden. His eyes opened in astonishment when he saw Tibs.

He nodded when he heard what had happened. "What did I say?"

I felt embarrassed, "I was just so worried."

"Where did you find him?" Mum asked delightedly when she saw him.

"Outside, look he's hurt his leg."

Mum bathed it, and made up a bed by the fire.

"We'll have to give him some of our milk until he is well enough to hunt for himself," she said, as she tucked him up.

THE LONG WINTER
Chapter 31

Tibs seemed to recover quite quickly from his injury. He must have been very scared because now he always came home at night. It was so cold Jacques and I didn't stay out long either. We hardly ever went to the den; the walk through the trees on dark cold afternoons was quite scary. We really went to see if Tomasz had been back, but there was no sign that he ever returned. Every night we read the Press, because we knew if he'd been caught it would be headline news.

"Let's hope he's found a new hiding place," Jacques said.

I nodded, "And that it's safe and snug."

One evening Max had come in to warm himself by our fire. I was sitting by the oil lamp reading when Dad asked; "Was the prisoner who escaped ever caught?"

There was a pause before Max answered, "No, there was not the time to search for him when the invasion was expected. Now it is that they think he is dead of his injuries, starved, or killed by a mine."

I looked up and saw him looking at me quizzically. I was certain that he'd guessed the truth, and quickly looked down at the page, but my face felt hot and pink, and all the letters seemed jumbled up.

When I told Jacques what had happened he was reassuring, "That's good news, it means the Germans aren't hunting for Tomasz, and our secret's safe with Max."

We were very thankful that we weren't responsible for Tomasz now, there was hardly any food, and so much work to do.

Luckily school ended very early in the afternoon, to save light and heat. As soon as we got home we pumped water for the next day. Then we walked around the lanes looking for twigs and branches blown down in the wind, and for the green plants, which the rabbits loved to eat.

When we came home we'd take the food to the shed. Jacques's favourite rabbit was Snowball, mine Blackberry They seemed to recognise us and came to the front of their hutches and snuffled at the wire whenever we appeared. As their doors were opened they would hop into our arms, and we gave them an extra portion of food as a reward.

On cold wet days, as soon as the chores were done, we went indoors. The house wasn't nearly as warm and cosy as it used to be, there was so little coal and wood. We didn't use the range any more, all the cooking was done on the dining room grate.

We'd sit as close to the warmth as possible. If I grumbled Jacques would say, "You should come to my house, that's really cold."

When we had tea Mum lit the oil lamp, we didn't often switch on the light because electricity was rationed.

In the evening, after Jacques went home, we sat in the firelight to save oil, and Mum told stories. Sometimes I'd listen to the crystal set, ready to hide it at a moment's notice if anyone came to the door. It was exciting because the Germans were being defeated. Grandpa said they were definitely losing the war.

All the same it didn't feel as if we were winning, the real problem was that every one was hungry. We were all getting thinner, and our clothes looked baggy. Even the Germans, who took most of the food we grew, and who'd been fatter than anyone else, were skinny.

Sometimes we saw German soldiers walking in the fields, looking for anything to eat. I knew they would find nothing; nearly every thing, which could be eaten, had disappeared.

One day in the autumn Dad had come back from the hospital and said, "It's very sad, eleven soldiers ate hemlock they found in the fields, and have all died of poisoning."

"I expect they were men who came from cities and wouldn't know the dangers in the country side," said Mum, sounding sorry for them.

When Grandpa heard he didn't sound at all sad, in fact he grinned and said, "They got what they deserved."

One night it was very windy, and I was woken up at dawn by a banging sound, looking out of the window I saw that the shed door was open, and blowing back and forth.

"Wake up, wake up, something's happened," I called to Mum and Dad.

We ran outside, Mum didn't even take out her curlers. We could see that the padlocks had been wrenched off the door.

Three of the hutches were open, and Smokey, Snuffles and Misty had gone. There was blood on the floor.

"The thieves must have been disturbed otherwise they wouldn't have left the other two rabbits," said Dad.

When Jacques heard what had happened he frowned, "Well, our rabbits survived, but I wonder for how much longer."

That evening Dad brought the hutches into the kitchen. The two rabbits were cowering inside.

"We're going to bring them here at night, we have to keep them safe."

Mum looked fed up, "You can't, they're smelly."

"Let's be thankful they're not pigs," I said, and we all laughed.

When people heard about the theft of the rabbits they weren't surprised, animals were disappearing every day.

One morning when Dad came home, he looked pale; "We had a lucky escape last night. It was very late and we were driving the ambulance when a group of ragged men with big sticks approached menacingly. I accelerated and they had to jump to the side." He had sounded scared when he said; "these people are thieves who are starving, they will murder for food."

"Who are the thieves?" I asked.

"Well it could be anyone, we are all so hungry, but I guess it's probably the Russians, they're the worst off."

When Max heard what had happened he said to Mum, "It is dangerous for you on the nights your husband works. I have for you a German Police whistle. If a thief ever comes, open the window and blow as loudly as you can. Help will come."

One day when we went to the farm everyone started whispering, while I pretended to read, but listened intently. Papa was talking about some neighbours, who lived just down the road from the farm.

"They were fed up with having vegetables stolen nearly every night from their fields, so they decided to keep watch. The thieves came back that very night, there was a fight, the farmer was murdered and his son badly injured.""

I felt shivery inside and Dad looked terribly anxious, and said, "We're all in great danger, we can't be too careful."

As soon as we arrived home I was sent into the living room while Mum and Dad whispered in the kitchen. I thought how stupid they were, I knew all about the danger surrounding us.

On the following days Dad was very busy making the house safer. First of all he put big bolts on the front and back doors. Then all the keys for downstairs doors were found and put in the locks. Next he made wooden wedges, which could be put under the doors to stop them opening.

Then he did the same at Westwood, and also for Mrs. Le Marquand.

"It's funny," said Jacques, "this should make me feel safer, but it actually makes me more scared."

The Feldpolizie whistle given by Max to Marianne's family.

THE BIG QUESTION
Chapter 32

During the cold dark days there was one thing that made us hopeful we might not starve, The Bailiff had been allowed to ask the Red Cross to send us food.

One day in the paper there was the news that a boat was on the way. Everyone we met talked of nothing else. Would there be food at last? We waited and waited but the boat didn't arrive.

" At least we have something," said Mum.

We did, it was cauliflower. There had been a fine crop in the top field, which the thieves hadn't found. Every day we ate cauliflower, as a vegetable at dinnertime, and cauliflower soup made with milk at suppertime. Jacques said that he had porridge and turnips every day.

The days passed and one morning Dad said, "We need some food, and I'm going to kill the white rabbit."

He looked at me, "You know I told you that it wasn't a pet." I nodded.

When I came home from school the hutch was empty.

I dreaded telling Jacques, but he only shrugged and said, "I hate war."

The next day when I went home there was the smell of rabbit stew, and my mouth watered. I pushed open the living room door. To my horror Mum was sitting in front of the grate, and for the first time in my life I saw her crying, tears were streaming down her face.

"I was just going to dish up our dinner when my hand slipped on the handle. The food tipped on the fire, the hearth and the rug," she sobbed.

I ran over and grabbed the spoon, and scooped up as much of the stew from the hearth and rug as possible. Luckily only a little had fallen into the fire.

When Dad came in we had what was left of the stew. It wasn't very nice as it had cinders in it, and bits of wool from the rug. But we all cleaned our plates, and wished there'd been more.

The next day Mum made another stew with what was left of the rabbit. She used lots of potatoes and vegetables from Mrs. Le Marquand and Grandpa. We divided the stew between all of us. I took some to Westwood, and some to Grandmère.

After dinner Jacques was in the garden looking very miserable. I guessed he was thinking of Snowball.

"Did you eat any of the stew?" I asked.

He nodded, "It is as Tomasz says, you eat anything if you are hungry."

Every day we wondered if the Red Cross boat would come. I hoped it would reach the island before my birthday, but it didn't. That was when we began to think that it might never arrive.

On my birthday morning there were some presents. The first to be opened was the book, 'Wind In The Willows,' from Mam and Papa Camp. In the second were raisins that Grandmamma had made from drying grapes from the greenhouse.

Last of all was a little present from Mum and Dad.

I was certain it was a brooch, and slowly took off the paper, inside there were three cubes covered in silver paper, and either the letters O or X on each side.

"What are they?" I couldn't remember seeing anything like them before.

" They're OXO cubes; they're made from meat. We had them before the war and they were quite cheap. We used to put them into meat dishes," Mum explained,"to give them a good flavour."

I bought these on the black market and they cost more than anything I've ever bought. They cost ten shillings each, that's thirty shillings altogether."

I was astonished, that was what Dad earned each week before the war; imagine a whole week's wages for three little cubes."

Mum took one of the cubes and broke it in half, put into a big cup and poured on boiling water.

"Sip it slowly because it is very rich, and you aren't used to rich food."

I tasted, it was salty and really delicious.

"Umm," I sighed, "it's the best thing I've ever tasted. Let's keep the rest to share, and put a pinch at a time, to flavour special dishes."

In the afternoon Jacques came to tea. He brought a present. It was a paint box, his paint box. I'd borrowed it to paint special paintings, and knew that it was one of his treasures.

"I think we can share this," I said. Jacques grinned happily.

It was a lovely party. First we had the party tea. We had half a boiled egg each, then biscuits made from the flour that I'd ground from wheat in the coffee grinder, and stewed apple. We didn't have a cake but we put the candles in a cabbage.

After tea it was dark, and we sat as close to the fire as possible and told ghost stories.

As Christmas drew nearer everyone said that a Red Cross ship was definitely coming. The days passed and there were rumours; there had been a storm and the ship had been lost, then, even worse, she'd hit a mine and sank.

"Whatever happens," Mum said, "we're going to celebrate Christmas as usual."

We brought in the little, 'well it wasn't so little now', Christmas tree and put up the decorations.

I was certain that there would be rabbit stew on Christmas day, and gave Blackberry extra cuddles.

It was the afternoon before Christmas Eve when we decided to go to the den. As we walked into the wilderness the sun shone through the bare branches of the trees, and there were even a few bright yellow flowers on the gorse bushes.

As we neared the den the leaves of the ivy were deep green and shiny. Turning the corner we saw the holly bush, beside the spring, covered in bright red berries.

There was no sign that Tomasz had been here recently, it smelt musty; and there was dust everywhere.

"Let's give it a good winter clean," I suggested.

We shook up the bracken and hay bed, then swept away the dust and cobwebs, and washed the dishes in the stream.

Every time we went outside a robin would fly down and perch on a nearby branch.

"Perhaps he's waiting for Tomasz," said Jacques.

Soon the den smelt fresh and clean, the bed looked comfortable, and the dishes sparkled. We agreed that if Tomasz returned this would be his Christmas present.

Closing the door we shivered, the sun had disappeared. It was dark and gloomy, the branches of the trees looked menacing, and twigs cracked under our feet as we walked. Everywhere there were shadows as the bushes moved in the wind.

We both breathed sighs of relief when we walked into the garden, and hurried into the kitchen. Blackberry's cage hadn't been brought in for the night so it was clear what had happened.

The next day was Christmas Eve. Mum and I went to the farm. "No meat this year," said Papa, "but Mam has packed up a few things for you."

We stayed for dinner and had boiled onions in white sauce, and a baked apple each for pudding.

When we arrived home we looked at what Mam had sent, there was big bottle of milk, and some cheese and butter.

Just then Dad arrived, "That looks good. There's no sign of the ship, we can only hope she does make it soon."

Going to bed that night it seemed unlikely that there would be any presents, but in the morning there was something by my toes. I sat up and felt, yes, there were some parcels.

I carried them into Mum and Dad's bedroom. Dad lit the candle and the first present was opened. There was a pair of mittens made from what looked suspiciously like white rabbit fur, and I hoped it wasn't Snowball. There was a jumper. I recognized the wool from other jumpers that that been knitted and re-knitted as I grew out of them. Next a drawing book and some charcoal, which probably had come from Mrs. Druit's shop in Trinity Square. Best of all, a book called The Old Curiosity Shop, which no one had written or scribbled in.

Breakfast was a special breakfast. There was the usual bowl of porridge, but this time there were some of my birthday raisins sprinkled on the top.

After we'd finished eating Dad said," I think there were a few flakes of snow." He unlocked the front door to have a look.

Suddenly he said, "Blow me! Where did this come from?"

He came back into the room and in his hand was a little carved cat. At that moment there was a knock on the door and Jacques rushed in. He was holding a wooden carving of a very cheeky robin.

Mum and Dad looked mystified.

"Who can have made these?" asked Dad.

Mum shook her head, "We don't know anyone who can carve wood like this."Jacques and I grinned at one another, the cat looked like Tibby Puss, and the robin looked like the robin at the den.

After breakfast Dad and I went to Westwood. Grandmamma was distraught, she didn't even say, "Happy Christmas."

"What are we going to do?" she asked. "There's no more gas on the island, it's run out. How am I going to cook?"

"Don't worry," said Dad. He placed some bricks on either side of the grate, put in newspaper and sticks, then went outside and came back with a little doorscraper, and rested it on the bricks.

When everything was in place he lit the fire, filled a kettle and put it on the top. "Now you can cook on that."

When the kettle boiled he took out a packet of tea, real tea. "This is your Christmas present; don't ask me where I got it".

Grandmamma fetched the teapot and put in a little tea. When it had brewed she poured out three cups. Grandmamma, Grandpa and Dad slowly drank.

"This is the first real tea I've had for years," Grandmamma said, and she actually smiled. Grandpa didn't even mention, 'black market.'

When the fire was glowing red Dad got two big potatoes from the kitchen, and put them in the fire with tongs. "Now this is your Christmas dinner. When they're cooked use some of this butter, which we got from the farm, and some of the cheese. Tomorrow I'll bring you some stew."

Grandmamma and Grandpa looked much happier. I gave them their presents. Grandpa had a scarf I'd knitted, Grandmamma had a painting of some flowers. Jacques's paint box was really useful, and we'd used it for nearly all our Christmas presents.

"We have a present for you," Grandpa said. It was the book 'Robinson Crusoe' which he used to read to me when I was small.

When we returned home Mum was laying the table for five people. "I've asked Mrs. Le Marquand and Jacques to join us, she's provided the carrots, turnips and parsnips."

There was a knock on the door, and Jacques came in holding his robin and put it next to my cat on the mantelpiece.

We sat down and had a delicious dinner of rabbit stew, and when we left the table we were, for the first time for weeks really full.

When the dishes were washed we sat in the firelight.

Dad said, "I bet the Red Cross boat comes soon."

We all felt cheerful, he sounded so certain. We asked riddles, and Dad told jokes, we roasted chestnuts and sang carols.

"Its almost curfew, it's time to go home," said Grandmère looking at the clock.

Dad switched on the fairy lights. Jacques and I picked up the cat and the robin and held them tightly. We smiled at one another. Now we knew that Tomasz was alive and well.

DANGER
Chapter 33

It was early in the morning, the day after Boxing Day when Dad came in, and called out excitedly, "The Red Cross ship is here. Let's go and have a look."

Jacques and I ran to get our bikes, and we set off. Lots of other people were also hurrying along.

"We won't get any food to-day," explained Dad, "but we'll be able to see the ship."

We weren't allowed onto the harbour, but we could see the boat. She was white, with huge red crosses painted at the front and back.

"Those crosses are there so she won't be attacked, and look, she has a blue and yellow flag. I can see her name, she's called the Vega," said Jacques.

"She must be a Swedish ship, because that's the Swedish flag," said Dad."

We felt very excited, but waiting for the food to be unloaded was even worse than waiting for Christmas.

At last there was a notice in the Press saying the food parcels could be collected from the local shop, where people were registered for their rations.

Mum, Grandmère, Jacques and I set off to Mrs. Robin's shop, at La Fosse. We kept meeting people carrying their parcels home. Most of them were happy and smiling, but Mrs. De Garis was crying.

"Why's she crying?" I asked.

"Tears of joy," said Mum.

Jacques and I looked at one another, he shrugged, "She's daft, I can't stop grinning."

Once again my dolls' pram was useful, we put the five parcels inside and wheeled them home.

While Jacques went into his house we carried the parcels, which were made of cardboard and had a red cross on the top, into the dining room and put them on the table.

Dad was waiting. He opened the first parcel; it was full of tins and packets.

"We haven't seen food like this for five years," said Mum, "and it all comes from Canada."

I read out what we had in each parcel, "6 oz chocolate, 20 oz biscuits, 20 oz butter, 20 oz dried milk, 6 oz prunes, 20 oz ham, 10 oz salmon, 14 oz corned beef, 8 oz sugar, 4 oz cheese, 16 oz marmalade, 8oz raisins, 4 oz tea, 5 oz sardines, 13 oz Spam, 3 oz soap, 1 oz salt and pepper."

"You sound just like Rat, in 'Wind In The Willows,' when they went on the picnic on the river bank," said Mum, "but whatever is Spam?"

"It must be some kind of meat made from ham," replied Dad, "anyway, what shall we have first?"

" A cup of real tea," said Mum. I had a cup of tea, but couldn't really see why Mum and Dad liked it so much; it didn't taste of anything special.

Next we had biscuits and creamy cheese, which was really delicious. Dad wouldn't let us eat much, he said that it would be dangerous to suddenly eat a lot of rich food, it might make us very ill.

As we finished eating there was a tap at the door, and Jacques came in.

"What did you eat first?" I asked.

"Biscuits and butter. Grandmère had a cup of tea, and I am going to have some chocolate at bedtime."

It was wonderful at bedtime. I felt really full, and unwrapped the chocolate, and had one square, I'd forgotten how delicious it tasted. I fell asleep thinking that this had been one of the best days of my whole life.

The next day we opened a tin of salmon. I looked at the salmon on my plate, it didn't look like any fish I'd ever seen. It was red, with some white pieces, which I pointed at, "What are these?"

"They're bones."

I tasted the fish, and scrunched up the bones

"Um, scrumptious, I hope we'll be able to have this when the war's over."

"It's very expensive, perhaps occasionally, as a great treat," Mum said.

The next evening we asked Max to supper.

"Poor fellow," said Dad, "he's practically starving."

It almost seemed like a party when we sat down at the table. Mum had made fishcakes with a little of the salmon.

"Oh so good," said Max, "but no one must know, there is big punishment if we eat Red Cross Food."

"Don't worry," said Dad, "no one knows, if they did we'd also be punished, we might never get any more Red Cross parcels."

When the dishes were washed we sat as close to the warmth of the fire as possible, drinking cups of tea.

"Let us hope this war ends soon, and you see your family," said Mum.

Max shook his head, "It is bad, very bad, there is much bombing in Germany."

That night in bed I thought about the bombing. Grandpa often talked about the war. He said that the Germans were losing, their armies driven back on all fronts, German towns were being blown to smithereens, and people were starving.

He sounded really pleased, and said that they were having a taste of their own medicine. I thought that was wrong, it must be terrible knowing your country and family are being bombed. Poor Freyda, I wondered if she hid under the stairs like we did when there were air raids.

The next day Jacques and I were in the kitchen and I asked, "Can we have some dried milk?"

Mum took down the tin with KLIM on the label, and put a little spoonful on two saucers. I looked at the tin and said, "Do you realize that KLIM, is milk spelt backwards?"

"No I didn't," Mum sounded astonished.

We took our saucers, and went into the living room dipping our fingers in the milk and sucking the powder off.

"Umm," murmured Jacques. Then he said, "The wooden animals Tomasz made were lovely, they were such good presents."

"I know," I agreed, "and we never gave him anything, except cleaning the den. Let's give him something now."

We thought and thought, "Chocolate," I suggested.

"Yes," agreed Jacques, "he won't have had any chocolate for years."

The next two nights we each saved our squares of chocolate. The following day we went into the wilderness for the first time since Christmas. Tomasz wasn't around, but he'd obviously been there. The blanket on the bed was untidy, and when Jacques touched the ashes they were still warm.

We opened the biscuit tin, there was nothing inside. I'd brought a piece of paper and a pencil, and wrote, 'thank you very much for the wooden animals, they were our best presents. We hope you like the chocolate; it is from the Red Cross Parcels. Love, Jacques and Marianne.'

We put the chocolate in the box, and the letter and a pencil, so he could write back. We returned a few days later. The hut was cold.

Jacques lifted the lid on the tin, and the chocolate had gone, but there was a note, 'Thank you for the chocolate, it was very good. I have a new hiding place, but hope to see you in the future. Tomasz'.

"I wonder where that is?" I said.

"It doesn't really matter as long as he has enough to eat," said

Jacques, " but let's hope we do see him again."

Weeks later the 'Vega' came back, and this time brought parcels from New Zealand. Best of all there was condensed milk in these parcels, and if no one was around Jacques and I would lift up the lid and dip our fingers in, and lick off the wonderful sweetness.

We made the food in the parcels last, but what we hadn't realized at first was that the parcels brought great danger. Every day we heard about robberies, people were attacked, and some even killed by starving men who roamed the island.

Now we our food in the bedroom. Often I would creep up and look at all the wonderful Red Cross food, then hold the tins and packets and read the labels.

I was thankful Dad had put on all the locks and bolts, and for greater safety we all slept in one bedroom. Tibs got what he had always wanted, he was allowed to sleep with us. He usually curled up by my feet, and he purred as I fell asleep.

But even with Tibs on the bed I hated the nights; there were always nightmares where soldiers and men were chasing me, and just before they caught me I would wake up crying and shouting. The worst nights of all were the nights when Dad was working at the Ambulance station.

It was on one of those nights when Mum and I were alone and sitting in the darkness, as close to the fire as possible, she said, "The fire is almost out, we'll go upstairs now, it will be much warmer in bed."

I held the candle and we walked to the back and front doors and checked that they were locked, and then pushed across the bolts. We went into the hall and Tibby Puss followed. We locked the downstairs doors, and pushed wedges underneath so it would be impossible to open them.

We walked up the stairs, the candle making flickering shapes on the wall. Tibby Puss ran ahead and into the bedroom. We followed and locked the door, put in the wedge, and Mum checked to see that the big carving knife was on the table, and that the whistle that Max had given us was hanging from the nail by the window.

It was so cold that we undressed and jumped into bed as quickly as we could, and snuggled up. Tibs was warm against my back as I looked out of the window. The moon was bright, and the dark clouds were edged in silver. Sometimes a cloud drifted across the face of the moon, and for a few minutes the room was in darkness.

It was early so Mum told stories of long ago, before the war, about her life on the farm, and the picnics that I could hardly remember on the beaches nearby.

I fell asleep, and then woke up, something had awakened me. I knew from her breathing that Mum was also awake, listening - there was someone in the garden.

First, the shed door was opened, but we knew there was nothing inside. Then there was the sound of feet on the gravel. After that it was quiet, so someone was walking on the grass towards the house.

Mum got out of bed and peeped out of the window. The moonlight was bright. She whispered, "There are two of them, and they are coming to the sitting room window."

Suddenly she threw open the bedroom window and blew the whistle as loudly as she could. I jumped out of bed, and saw the men running away.

We got back into bed, my heart was thumping, and we were both shivering, Mum said, with cold, but I knew it was fear. We cuddled up together, and I held Tibs in my arms.

When Dad came back in the morning he looked scared and angry when he heard all that had happened.

Mum said, "Max told us that help would come immediately we blew the whistle, but it didn't."

"Well it drove the thieves away," I said, "but if they had got in I think they would have come up and stolen the food and hurt us."

Dad gave me a hug, "Don't worry, nothing's going to happen."

The Red Cross Ship 'Vega'.

A Red Cross parcel.

WILL HE? WON'T HE?
Chapter 34

Jacques was surprised when he heard about the midnight thieves; he hadn't even heard the whistle. We were both scared going to bed because there were more and more attacks and murders, and I wondered if the thieves would come back.

"Don't worry, the war will soon be over," Dad said reassuringly, "the Germans armies are losing all their battles, and being driven back to Berlin where Hitler is hiding, and it won't be long before he's beaten. When he's defeated the war will be over."

It began to be less frightening when the evenings were lighter; winter was nearly over, and it began to feel a bit safer.

We still had our food parcels, but there was less and less food on the island. We even ate boiled stinging nettles, they didn't taste very nice, but I was surprised, they didn't sting at all.

One evening there was a notice in the Press, there would be no more bread until further notice.

"Well," said Jacques, "I didn't think I'd ever miss that grey sour bread, but it's awful having nothing with the jam from our parcels.

One day when I came home from school Mum was waiting by the back door.

"Just come and see what we have," she called.

I ran into the living room, and on the table was an enormous loaf of white bread. I stared in astonishment; surely before the war loaves hadn't been as large as this?

"The Vega brought flour that comes from wheat grown in Canada," Mum said, "it's different from wheat in England, it makes special bread, I've never seen bread like this, it's almost as large as a football."

I watched as she cut off the crust at the end of the loaf, spread it with butter, and we sat down and ate.

Mum sighed with contentment, "This is what I've dreamed of from almost the beginning of the Occupation, white bread and butter."

Now I could understand her longing, it was wonderful, indeed the best food in the world.

When Dad returned he sat down and savoured every mouthful, then he said, "What would we have done without the Red Cross? Last time the 'Vega' brought things for the hospital, if the supplies hadn't arrived patients would have died."

It wasn't long before there was a really sunny day, and Mum asked, "Would you like a picnic?"

Jacques and I nodded enthusiastically, and set off with some of the wonderful bread, some carrots, cheese and Spam.

"Let's go to the den," I suggested, and we walked into the wilderness.

The sky above the trees was blue, and buds on the trees were opening. All around was the singing of birds, and suddenly the robin was fluttering from branch to branch in front of us.

Glancing back we saw that Tibby Puss was following.

"He knows that it feels like spring, and he's enjoying the sunshine too," said Jacques.

We came to the den and pushed open the door, there was no trace that Tomasz had returned.

"Well," I said, "I do hope he's all right, and he hasn't been captured or blown up by mines."

"I guess he'll survive," said Jacques, "he said he'd found a new hiding place, but it's strange he hasn't been back. Anyway this will be our own private den again, but he'll be welcome if he does come."

We sat, leaning against the wall in the sun, and Tibs curled up between us. We took out our picnic. "Isn't it strange," I said as we ate every morsel, "that men from the Red Cross face the danger of being killed, blown up by mines or bombed, to bring us food to save our lives. At the same time German planes bomb England, and English planes bomb Germany, and they're all trying to kill people just like us."

Jacques nodded, "Yes, and Tomasz would fight and kill Max if he could, and Max will have to fight British soldiers if they come to Guernsey."

" I really don't know who are real friends, and who are enemies," I said. "Some brave Guernsey men printed G.U.N.S. but they were betrayed. And others told the Germans about local people who had wireless and crystal sets so they were caught and punished.

Grandmère and my Grandparents hate Germans, like Max and Dr Hodeige, and yet both of them are friends with Mum and Dad, and with us."

We gave up trying to puzzle it out, and set to work spring-cleaning.

"Tomasz will like staying here if he comes back," I said brushing down cobwebs.

We were both exhausted when we'd finished cleaning, but it was worth it. We looked proudly around before hurrying home for tea.

A few weeks later, in the evening, Max knocked on the door, he rarely came now, and Mum invited him to supper. We had Spam and some of the white bread.

"That was good, I thank you," said Max.

He sat in silence for a moment and then carried on, "Today is twentieth of April, Hitler's birthday. Today we went to cinema Gaumont."

I remembered the Gaumont cinema, that was where we'd seen, 'The Wizard Of Oz,' and wondered if Max had been to see a film.

He almost seemed to read my thoughts. "We saw not a film, it was Admiral Hüffmeier; he say we should fight for the Führer, for our wives and children to the end."

I knew who Admiral Hüffmeier was, he was in charge of the islands, and I also knew that everyone hated him.

"What will happen to you think?" Dad asked.

"I know not, many soldiers ill with starvation, many not want to fight, but the Admiral he proud and strong."

When Max returned home Dad said "There's no doubt now, the end is in sight."

Mum looked worried, "If he doesn't surrender the British will have to attack, and we'll be in terrible danger."

When I told Jacques he was reassuring, "We don't need to worry, if there is fighting we will bring all our relations to the den, and we'll be safe."

Everyone was talking about the war, and seemed excited and frightened all at the same time, wondering what was going to happen next.

On the way home from school, a few days later, Lesley and Muriel were walking behind me calling out, "Marianne's a scarecrow," and pointing and laughing.

Suddenly they stopped because Stan Workman, who used to work at the vinery, and who had taught me to tie shoelaces, came around the corner.

He grinned at me and said, "Have you heard, Hitler is dead?"

I ran home as fast as I could, and told Mum the news. She didn't seem to really believe it, and was just taking the crystal set from the hiding place in the armchair when Dad came running in shouting, "Hitler is dead, I heard it on the B.B.C."

We hurried to Westwood and as we arrived the Press came. There it was on the front page, it said: THE FÜHRER IS DEAD.

"Is the war over?" I asked.

Grandpa said, "Not yet, someone else is in charge, but it won't be long now."

Every time I went to Westwood Grandpa seemed to be reading the latest news. On the fifth of May he read;

"The Führer died at the head of his men, those valiant supporters who defended Berlin to the last.

The legend of Adolf Hitler will be eternal. It is a talisman for Germany's youth, and a symbol of Germany's greatness, a greatness that will live on, and with which the name of Adolf Hitler will be forever associated-as the founder and creator of the Greater Reich."

Grandpa snorted with indignation, "His name will live on for ever as one of the most evil and wicked men the world has ever known, The article is all lies, on the B.B.C. it says that he killed himself hiding in his bunker. He was a coward.

Remember Marianne, until your life's end, this wonderful and exciting time of liberation."

Jacques and I didn't have to go to school now; we were waiting to see what was going to happen. Everyone was excited, but also frightened, waiting in suspense. Would Admiral Hüffmeier hold out to the end, or would he surrender?

The next day Jacques and I knocked on Max's door, but he didn't open it although we were certain that he was inside. In fact there were no Germans around.

Dad took out the crystal set, "We won't hide this any more, no one will try to stop us listening,"and he put on the headphones.

Just then Jacques knocked on the door and came in.

His eyes opened with astonishment. "I didn't know you had a set, I thought we were friends and told each other everything."

"I couldn't tell you, Mum and Dad made me promise," I explained.

Dad was listening to the set when suddenly he jumped up, and waved his arms in the air.

"This is what we've been waiting for, tomorrow, May the eighth is going to be, 'Victory in Europe Day,' the official end of the war," he paused, "but will it be the end of the war for us?"

Above: Admiral Hüffmeier. The man who wouldn't say yes.
Below: Great celebrations when the British troops arrive.

LIBERATION
Chapter 35

The first thing I thought when I woke up was, the war is over, everyone's happy, but what about us? The morning passed really slowly, and after we'd eaten dinner Jacques came in, "Can we go and see Max?" I asked.

"You don't go anywhere until we know what's happening," replied Dad sternly.

Suddenly there was the rattle of the letterbox, and the Press fell onto the mat. "Look," said Mum, "it says **'FLY YOUR FLAGS AT HALF PAST THREE,'** the Germans have stated that the war is officially over in the Channel islands. It says we have to listen to the wireless at three o'clock this afternoon."

"We haven't any flags have we?" I asked

"No," replied Dad, "we haven't, but Grandpa may have, we'll go to Westwood to find out.

Jacques do you want to come with us?"

I wasn't sure if he would want to come, he wasn't very keen on meeting Grandmamma, but he was nodding enthusiastically.

We set off on our bikes.

"Do we still have to cycle on the right?" I asked as we passed the place where I'd knocked the German off his bike.

"Yes," said Mum, "or it will be utter confusion."

When we arrived Grandpa was waiting for us by the gate. I remembered we'd been standing there when we saw the tanks pass, and how scared I'd been.

We went inside, and for once Grandmamma looked happy, she even smiled at Jacques.

To my astonishment, there, on the sideboard, where it had stood before the war, was the wireless set.

Grandpa said, "When they told us to give in the sets I hid ours under the window seat in the attic."

I was surprised; the front of the seat does not look in the least like a cupboard. I'd played in the attic so many times, and never suspected a thing.

Grandpa was still talking, "I used to creep up to the attic at night and listen; only Grandmamma and Dad knew what I was doing."

Now I understood how he always seemed to know what was happening in the rest of the world. It must have been awful for Grandmamma, she worried all the time. If the set had been found Grandpa would certainly have been sent to prison, and he was so ill he might never have come out.

At a few minutes to three o'clock we all sat near the wireless set in absolute silence. Suddenly Mr. Churchill declared that the war had been won, and at the end of the speech he said, **"And our dear Channel Islands are also to be freed today,"** and we all clapped.

I remembered that we'd been in this room when war was declared, and how frightened everyone had been then, now everyone was so happy, smiling and laughing.

Grandpa said, "Come on, there's work to be done," and we followed him out to the shed.

He got a stepladder, and opened it. "Hold it steady," he said, as he climbed precariously up to the rafters. He took down an enormous folded Union Jack, which he'd hidden.

We went back inside, and upstairs to the bedroom. He opened the window, and then closed the sash on the flag, so that it hung down to the front door.

"You'd better be careful, there may still be Germans walking around, there are no British soldiers here yet," said Grandmamma.

Grandpa took no notice, he was euphoric, "It's official now, that terrible Admiral Hüffmeier must have given in, so what do I care!"

Then he turned to me, "You'll remember this day all your life Marianne, and when you're an old lady I'm certain everyone in Guernsey will still be celebrating Liberation Day, on May the ninth."

On the way home we stopped by Max's house, and knocked, but he didn't come to the door.

"He's gone," said Jacques, "and we didn't have a chance to say good-bye."

When Mum and Dad went in to get tea Jacques and I hurried through the wilderness to the den. We both wanted to see Tomasz, to know that he was safe and well, but the den was still deserted.

We walked slowly back, we didn't say anything, but we were frightened something awful must have happened to him, because we were certain he would have wanted to share the victory with us.

The next day Dad came back early in the morning, very excited, "There are two British war ships outside the harbour, and lots of people are in town, even though the soldiers haven't landed."

As soon as we'd finished breakfast we went to get our bikes, and Jacques whispered, "Let's look for Tomasz, if he's all right he's bound to be in town," and I nodded in agreement.

We hurried to town; there were Union Jacks and flags everywhere, and not a Swastika in sight. As we reached the harbour we could see the big ships, and suddenly there was the sound of cheers, and there were British soldiers marching along the road.

The soldiers couldn't move very quickly, men were shaking their hands and patting their backs, and women were hugging and kissing them.

Jacques and I ran to the soldiers, and to our surprise they gave us handfuls of sweets and chocolate, and there were cigarettes for the adults.

We went everywhere, all the time people were shouting, some people were even singing and dancing, there were church bells ringing, it is the most exciting thing that has ever happened in my whole life, but there was no sign of Tomasz anywhere.

The next few days were wonderful. More and more soldiers were coming to the island, there were hundreds of them, and they were bringing food and things we desperately needed.

We even saw a boat in the entrance to the old harbour, and when the tide went out the ship was resting on the sea bed. We watched in amazement as the whole front opened, and trucks drove out across the harbour floor, carrying great packages, up the slip and on to the road.

"How can it float?" asked Jacques

Dad explained that when the front was pulled up there was a seal, so the sea couldn't get in.

Jacques and I wandered around town, while Mum and Dad chatted to old friends, and to the soldiers.

A group of soldiers were passing and threw us some sweets, one soldier held out a packet, "Do you like gum?" he asked.

"What's gum?" we said together.

"You've never tasted gum?" the soldier looked amazed. "Well you chew it, but you don't swallow it."

We took the packet, and undid the wrapping, inside were what looked like white sweets. We sniffed, and both said, "Peppermint" at the same time, and popped them into our mouths.

"It's true," said Jacques, chewing vigorously, "it doesn't go away."

Then we saw some children running up to soldiers and calling out, "Got any gum chum?"

"Let's try that," Jacques suggested, and it worked. Soon we had packets of gum, as well as sweets.

I said to Jacques. "It's really lucky. Grandmamma isn't here, she'd be so shocked, because she says, 'don't ask for what you want, wait to be asked,' and she'd think that chewing gum is common."

Jacques almost fell off his bike laughing, "I'm just imagining her face, she'd look like a cow with stomach ache."

Soon we had huge balls of gum, and we stuck them under the table at meal times, and on our bed posts at night, but all the adults we knew kept saying, "Get rid of that disgusting stuff."

Every day was a holiday. Mum and Dad had made friends with some British soldiers, and at night they came to our house, and played cards. Sometimes it seemed like a party as Dad played the piano and they sang songs.

They talked a lot about the war, but no one mentioned Max or Dr. Hodeige, or Hubert who had sat in this very room, and I wondered where they were.

Dad had said that some Germans were going to be sent to prisoner-of-war camps, and it might be years before they went home. Others were going to stay on the island to clear all the minefields, and that was very dangerous.

As everyone sang louder and louder I thought of Freyda, and how awful it must be not to have her Dad home.

Then about Tomasz, was he still alive? If he was, where could he be?

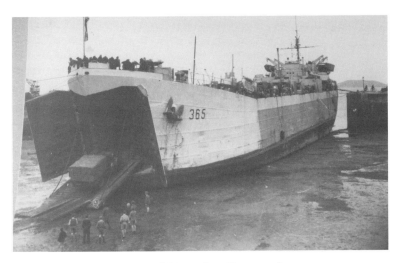

A Royal Navy landing craft.

PEACE AND

How the German Capitulation
was Signed.

Five years, eight months and four days after it began, at 11 o'clock on the morning of Sunday, September 3rd, 1939, the war in Europe was ended at 2.41 (normal Greenwich time) on Monday morning, May 7th, 1945, by the unconditional surrender of Germany to Great Britain, the United States of America and Soviet Russia.

For the Island of Guernsey this historic moment meant more than the cessation of hostilities. It meant, too, that the 23,000 Islanders who remained here after the evacuation are freed from the captivity imposed upon them by the German armed forces which invaded this, a part of the only mere fragment of British territory they could ever capture and possess, on the night of Sunday, June 30th, 1940. With the submission of Germany to the Allies, the Occupation is over.

It was a few minutes after 6 o'clock on Sunday evening, May 6th, that the news flashed around the Island that Peace was imminent. Those still in possession of radio receiving sets heard at that time the brief, but pregnant assurance that the Prime Minister was expected very soon to broadcast the news for which the whole world was waiting, and that His Majesty the King would afterwards speak to his subjects everywhere in the British Empire and Commonwealth.

Throughout Monday the tension in Guernsey was electric. Everyone was on the edge of expectancy. Excitement was subdued, but intense, and all were conscious of momentous events impending.

Then, again at 6 o'clock in the evening, came the glorious tidings. Germany signed her capitulation to the three big Powers at nineteen minutes to three o'clock (G. M. T.) on Monday

(Continued on Page 4)

LIBERATION

The King calls Nation to
"The Final Task."

His Majesty King George VI. broadcast from London at 9 p.m. Tuesday to all the peoples of the British Empire and Commonwealth of Nations. This is the full text of his address:—

To-day we give thanks to Almighty God for a great deliverance. Speaking from the Empire's oldest capital city, war-battered, but never for one moment daunted or dismayed, speaking from London, I ask you to join with me in that act of thanksgiving. Germany the enemy who drove all Europe into war, has been finally overcome. In the Far East we have yet to deal with the Japanese, a determined and cruel foe. To this we shall turn with the utmost resolve and with all our resources. But, at this hour, when the dreadful shadow of war has passed far from our hearths and homes in these islands, we may at least make one pause for thanksgiving, and then turn our thoughts to the tasks all over the world which peace in Europe brings with it. Let us remember those who will not come back—their constancy and courage in battle, their sacrifices and endurance in the face of a merciless enemy. Let us remember the men in all the Services and the women in all the Services who have laid down their lives. We have come to the end of our tribulation, and they are not with us at the moment of our rejoicing. Then, let us salute, in proud gratitude, the great hosts of the living who have brought us to Victory. I cannot praise them to the

(Continued on Page 2)

EXPLORATION
Chapter 36

It was a week after Liberation and we were having a wonderful time. Best of all there was no school, and Dad was taking a few days holiday.

"I think we should go exploring," he said.

"Exploring where?" I asked.

"To see some of the things the Germans left behind," he replied mysteriously.

It sounded exciting, and we set off on our bikes.

"I keep knocking my chin with my knees," Jacques said, as we puffed up a hill

"Me too," I agreed, "but we're much too big for our bikes. We had them when we were very young, that's five years ago, but they're better than nothing. I'd rather cycle than walk."

But I was luckier than Jacques, months before the inner tube on his bike had worn out, and Dad had patched it up, but it wouldn't keep the air in, so he'd filled it with sand. That made pedalling really difficult, and we had to wait for him when we went up hills.

Dad suddenly stopped at what looked like a cottage, on the L'Eree road, but then I saw that it wasn't real. There were two painted windows, in one there was picture of a flower pot, with a geranium inside, in the other a black cat.

"That's camouflaged so that it looked exactly like a house, really it's a bunker, that's a place where soldiers hide, and keep ammunition and guns," Mum said. "The British pilots took lots of photos of the island, and they probably thought this really was a cottage."

We carried on cycling in the warm sunshine, and at last we came to L'Eree beach. At the side there was what looked like an enormous hill, but when we were near we saw that it was a very high tower that had been camouflaged. It was covered in wire mesh, and that was covered in lumps of something hard, painted brown and green, so it looked as if plants were growing.

We went in through a heavy armoured door. A ladder that went up and up. We started to climb, and got off at each floor and explored. There were big slits where soldiers could fire guns, and there was a telescope that pointed out to sea.

Halfway up the ladder stopped on one side, and continued on the opposite wall, right over a tremendous drop to the bottom. Mum was too scared to continue, but with Dad underneath, ready to catch us if we slipped, Jacques and I crossed over and climbed to the very top.

There was a gun, that pointed up, and which could be turned around. "That's an anti-aircraft gun, there were lots more all over the island," Dad said, "That's what we heard when they fired at British planes, and we used to hide in our cupboard under the stairs."

We were so high up we could see for miles. There were beaches stretching far away on either side.

Jacques pointed, "Look, there are gun emplacements and bunkers right along the coast."

He was right; I could see them.

"Hitler was so sure the British were going to send soldiers here, to get the islands back for Britain, he used the slave workers to built huge fortifications to stop them. There are minefields too. The British wouldn't have stood a chance if they'd tried to land," Dad explained.

I was really glad that horrible Vice Admiral Hüffmeier had given in.

When we climbed down we had a picnic of ham and tomato sandwiches. I longed for the day when the mines were gone, and we could go down to the beach.

The next few days we went all over the island. We saw a gigantic gun at the Mirus battery, and at the side was what looked like a cottage but was really a bunker.

"Cor, isn't that gun big," Jacques said.

It was absolutely huge, much longer than a bus.

" It's from a Russian battle ship, and is capable of firing shells thirty miles out to sea, so it could attack ships far away," Dad said.

I said, "Perhaps that's what we heard when the guns roared louder than thunder," and Dad nodded.

Another day we went to Jerbourg Point, which was near our cottage. In the distance there was the coast of France, like a smudge on the horizon.

There was a large bunker and inside a huge telescope. I looked through, and there was the French coast. I could see the houses, and even a lorry going along a road, it was truly amazing.

When Jacques looked through the viewfinder, he said, "I wouldn't have wanted to be a sailor on a British ship between here and France, you'd be blown up in a minute."

The most exciting thing we did was going into the tunnels. Dad told us there were miles and miles of tunnels all over the island, going from one bunker to another, and into gun emplacements.

We usually went down steps, and the light would fade behind us. In front there would be pitch-blackness. We had torches that only lit up the passage a little way ahead, and we made shadows on the walls,

There was a musty smell, and the concrete walls felt damp. We usually whispered because our voices echoed. I kept close to Mum, just in case someone, or something, jumped out and grabbed me. I noticed Jacques kept very close to Dad.

In some tunnels there were rooms at the sides, and we went into them. Sometimes there were beds, cupboards, and furniture.

"Here's some of the things that the Germans took when houses were taken over," Mum said, "and it was here soldiers stayed when they were on duty."

In one room there were words painted on the wall. In another a painting of hills, forests and a lake. There was a table on which were plates, cups, and playing cards.

I suddenly remembered what Grandpa had told us.

"We must be careful, in the Great War, things like these were booby trapped, and if they were picked up they exploded, and people were killed."

Dad shrugged his shoulders, "I'm sure it's safe, lots of local people are going into the tunnels and bunkers," but I noticed that no one touched anything.

As we were walking out Jacques whispered, "Do you think Tomasz is hiding in the tunnels?"

I shook my head, "Why would he do that?"

Jacques looked sad, "I don't know, it's just so strange that he hasn't come to see us."

One day Dad said, "Just one more visit underground, to the biggest tunnel of all," We set off, and came to a big door that led into a gianormous tunnel in the side of a hill.

"This is the underground hospital," Dad said.

We put on the torches and went in slowly. The large tunnel went on and on into the blackness, but there were side tunnels, and wards. It looked a real hospital; there was even an operating theatre.

Mum sighed, "I keep thinking about the poor starving slave workers, digging these tunnels through rock, building the towers and the bunkers. They were dressed in rags, in the freezing cold of winter, and the scorching heat of summer."

"Lots of them were injured," Dad said, "many died, it was terrible."

Poor Tomasz, I thought, poor, poor, Tomasz.

It was really good to get out into the sunshine; we were all shivering, and not only with cold.

"If the British had come to liberate us the hospital would have been full of injured soldiers," Mum said, "and Max would have been looking after them."

"What about us?" I asked.

Dad shook his head, there weren't any shelters for civilians, and I don't think the cupboard under the stairs would have been much good. We would have been lucky to survive."

L'Eree tower climbed by the children.

Above: The Mirus cottage camouflaging the Mirus gun.
Below: The gigantic Mirus gun.

THE PARTY
Chapter 37

It was a couple of days later when Mum said, "I think we should have a family party to celebrate Liberation. It will be like old times, because now we have food in the larder."

The day arrived; it was bright and sunny, and we were all up early to prepare. Dad went off and returned with an enormous crab. I kept out of the way; hating it when the crab was put in the boiling water.

I decided to decorate the rooms, and cut bunches of roses, and filled every vase, and put them on the widow sills, the mantle piece and the tables. The whole house was filled with the scent.

Next I helped Mum lay the table with the best lace tablecloths, and dishes. Then we made scones, a sponge cake, and Guernsey Gaûche, which is really like a fruit loaf. Last of all we got out bottles of ginger beer.

Dad had been busy getting the deckchairs, and dusting the garden seat. He put them in the shade of the apple trees.

We had a very quick dinner of cheese in jacket potatoes, and then we washed up.

"Before we change come and sit down for a moment," Dad said.

I was puzzled, he seemed serious, and I wondered if he'd found out about Tomasz. But to my surprise he said, "I don't think you've been very happy at the Convent for a while, am I right?"

I was amazed; I'd never said a word about how unhappy I'd been, they had too many other things to worry about.

I nodded my head.

"Good, I've told Reverend Mother you won't be back. You're going to the Girls' School in Town in September.

Now I think we'd better hurry and wash, and get dressed in our best clothes."

I couldn't believe it, I was so happy I thought I'd burst. Never to see Miss Sanders again, and never share a classroom with Lesley and Muriel. I was sorry that I wouldn't be with Jane and Iris, but decided we'd meet at weekends. It was the best news Dad could have given me.

I ran upstairs and danced around the bedroom as I dressed.

We all went into the garden and waited. After a while there was the sound of a car. Uncle Bill drove up in a car he'd borrowed, which had been hidden in a barn all through the war.

He opened the door, and out stepped Grandmamma in her best dress and hat, Grandpa followed smiling happily.

We sat in the garden, and Tibby Puss immediately came and jumped up on Grandpa's lap, purring contentedly.

We were all sitting drinking ginger beer when there was the sound of a door opening. Adele came out of her front door, walked down her path, and into the road.

I was just lifting my hand to wave when Grandmamma caught it and hissed, "Have nothing to do with that woman, she's no better than she should be; going around with Germans.

Women like her are called Jerry Bags. No one should talk to anyone who had anything to do with the Germans, they should be driven away from the island."

I was wondering what she would say if she knew about Max, Dr Hodeige and Huburt, when there was the sound of trotting hoofs, and around the corner came Punch, pulling the trap. Papa was holding the reins, and Mam was at his side. They were also dressed in their Sunday best.

Papa tied Punch up by the gate, and he immediately started to eat the grass on the hedge.

Mam walked up the path holding some letters, waving and smiling. I'd never seen her looking so happy.

"Everyone is well, and they're all coming back home to Guernsey, " she called.

It was wonderful, so many people coming back. Mam and Papa's daughters, my aunts, and Uncle Horace's wife, and three cousins.

I wondered what it would be like to meet these cousins. I could remember baby John David, because I'd wished that he had been left behind, rather than Scottie, who'd been eaten.

I could vaguely remember Dennis, but of course I never knew Anne, she was born in England, and was five years old. Her Dad had never seen her.

Grandmère and Jacques came into the garden.

Jacques was grinning." We've had a letter from my mother and father, they are well, and coming soon to Guernsey."

Grandpa said, "We've also had good news, we have the vinery once again, so we are back in business."

It was wonderful, so much good news in one day.

Everyone was talking as they stood up, and walked to the dining room. The food looked delicious. There was the crab, a bowl of salad with lettuce, tomatoes, cucumber, slices of hard-boiled eggs, and on the top some brightly coloured nasturtium petals.

There were plates of thin bread and butter, scones, jam, and best of all Mam had brought bowls of clotted cream, the most delicious food in the world.

I remembered that Grandmamma said that children should be seen, and not heard, so I ate my food and listened. Jacques and I kept smiling at one another, as everyone talked about all they were going to do in the next few weeks, and all the people they longed to see.

It was so good. All of us had something to celebrate, everyone was happy because there was no more danger. We all had enough to eat, and no one talked about the war, it really was over.

When we'd finished eating Uncle Bill arrived, and had a cup of tea.

Now it seemed like a real party. There was laughter and jokes, and even Grandmamma laughed. I tried to remember if I'd ever seen her laugh before.

At six o'clock they all walked down the path. Grandmamma and Grandpa climbed into the car, and waved as they moved off.

"Your Mother does remind me of Queen Mary," Mum said to Dad. I'd seen pictures of Queen Mary and thought she looked stuck up, as if there was a nasty smell under her nose.

Jacques was standing by Punch, "I gave him some carrots, and he ate them all," he told Papa.

"Jolly good, would you like to drive us up the lane?"

Jacques nodded enthusiastically. He sat between Mam and Papa on the seat, and I sat behind. Papa gave him the reins, Jacques said "Gee up," and off we went.

We drove all the way to the Forest Road, and sometimes Punch trotted.

"Well, we've come quite a way, I think we'd better stop now, you did very well," said Papa.

I waited while he took the reins, and noticed he put something into Jacques's hand.

We stood and waved good-bye. Jacques opened his hand, and there was half-a-crown.

"Good," he said, "I can start saving for a horse. When I grow up I'm going to work with horses."

We walked slowly back through the winding lanes in the evening sunshine, "This has been a good day," I said.

Jacques nodded in agreement, "The best ever!"

TRUE OR FALSE?
Chapter 38

The day after the picnic Jacques came round early, "I can't come out this morning. Grandmère is going to spring-clean ready for Ma Mère and Mon Père, even though we haven't any idea when they're coming." He gave a great sigh, "and I've got to help."

He looked really fed up as he walked away.

I wandered out into the lane. This was a perfect day to feel so happy. The sun was shining, the stream gurgled on its way to the sea, and the birds were singing fit to bust.

I turned the corner and saw Lesley walking towards me. She came and stood directly in front of me, so that I had to stop. She smiled, a mean, cruel smile.

She spoke slowly. "My parents say that I am not allowed to play with you, in fact, I shouldn't even speak to you.

Your mother, father and you, are all 'Jerry Lovers'. Soon you won't have any friends at all."

My heart began to beat fast, "That's not true, we're not 'Jerry Lovers'."

"Oh yes you are, my mother and father say that the Jerries, our enemies, used to come to your house all the time. They're going to see Reverend Mother to have you expelled."

My face was getting red. I yelled, "I wouldn't play with you, or talk to you even if you were the last person on earth. Anyway I'm not going back to the Convent, but to a school in town."

Lesley retorted, as quick as lightning, "Well, they will all know about you, and you won't have any friends. They'll probably expel you anyway."

I turned away, "I hate you, and your family. I don't care what you say."

The trouble was that I did care, and ran away as fast as possible. My thoughts were spinning, my stomach was churning, and my hands were hot and clammy.

I ran and ran until I reached the wilderness. Walking towards the den imaginary voices were shouting, 'Jerry lover, Jerry lover, Jerry lover.'

I sat on the grass with my back to the wall of the den and thought. Were we 'Jerry lovers'? Are we 'Jerry lovers'? What are 'Jerry lovers'? Are 'Jerry lovers' as bad as 'Jerry Bags'?

Max, Dr. Hodeige and Huburt didn't seem like enemies, they were friends who helped us. The German soldiers, who hit and starved the slave workers, were evil. The local people who told the Germans about the wireless sets, and who stole and hoarded food were wicked.

What would happen when I went to the new school? I choked back tears. Perhaps no one would be my friend.

What could I do?

It was impossible tell Mum, because she was always so worried about what people thought of her, and she would be as unhappy as me.

It would be useless to tell Dad, he'd go round to Lesley's parents, 'to sort it out,' and make it even worse.

What if Grandmamma and Grandpa found out, they'd be terribly ashamed and possibly say, "It serves you right; you've got what you deserve."

There was nothing I could do.

It was time for dinner so I washed my face, and walked slowly home.

When I walked in Mum asked, "Is anything the matter?"

I shook my head, and sat down and tried to eat.

"You don't look very well," Mum said, "probably the excitement has been too much. I think you should stay in and rest."

I couldn't sleep that night. The next day I didn't go out to see

Jacques, because I couldn't share this terrible secret, even with him.

It was when we were having tea the next evening that there was a loud knock at the front door. Dad jumped up, and I followed.

He opened the door. To my astonishment there was a policeman, an English officer and a soldier, and between them was Tomasz!

"Excuse me, Sir," the policeman was saying, when I called out, "Tomasz," and ran and hugged him.

"I think," said the officer, "that we should go indoors and talk."

"I have to get Jacques, he'll want to see Tomasz," I said.

Hurrying next door I called, "Come quickly, come quickly." Jacques and Grandmère followed me.

Jacques gasped when he saw Tomasz, and then he couldn't stop grinning.

We all sat down, and Mum, Dad, and Grandmère looked extremely puzzled.

"I think you should tell us all about this prisoner," the officer said looking at Jacques and me.

I started at the beginning, about the slave workers, and Tomasz being injured, and how we'd hidden him."

"Where did you hide him?" asked Dad.

So he had to be told about the wilderness, and I felt sorry that our secret den wasn't a secret any more.

Then I explained how we'd looked after him, and brought him food.

"Often their food," interrupted Tomasz.

"We had to disguise him," said Jacques, "so we gave him some of Grandpère's clothes, we hope you won't be angry," and he looked at Grandmère. She just smiled.

I carried on," We didn't see Tomasz after New Year, but he gave us the carved cat and robin at Christmas."

"So that's where they came from," said Dad. "Mum and I have racked our brains trying to solve that mystery."

The officer said, "Well, it seems that the prisoner has been telling us the truth, we believed that he was a German soldier in disguise, trying to hide from a crime."

"Please can you stay and have a cup of tea while Tomasz tells us what happened to him?" I pleaded.

The officer nodded, "That would be most acceptable, we'd like to hear the story."

As we sat drinking tea Tomasz told us that a farmer, Mr. Mahaut, and his daughter Catherine, had hidden him in a barn. In return he had helped in tasks where he couldn't be seen.

He paused, and then said, "Catherine and I want to be married. When this is allowed we want you," and he nodded at me, "to be the bridesmaid." He looked at Jacques, "and you to be the best man, and you will both be the guests of honour."

I gave a little jump of excitement. Jacques turned bright red; but he was nodding enthusiastically.

"What happens now?" Dad asked the officer.

"Well, it will be a matter of months to sort out the paper work," he replied, "and then I expect the Guernsey authorities will permit the marriage."

The following morning a reporter from the Press came to my house, and we had to tell the story, then he took some photographs.

The next day the Press arrived, and there were photographs of Jacques and me. There was a huge headline: CHILD HEROES SAVE SLAVE WORKER FROM CERTAIN DEATH.

Underneath was the story of all that had happened.

As we sat reading the phone rang again and again, all our family and friends wanted to congratulate us.

After a while I said to Mum, " Please, can you take the calls so we can go out?"

She was really happy to do that; my Mum did like a good old gossip.

We wandered up to the den, and sat in the sun. It wasn't long before Tibby Puss found us.

I told Jacques all about Lesley, and being called a 'Jerry lover'.

"I wondered what was the matter," he said, "I knew you must be miserable when you wouldn't come out."

"I'm not miserable now. I hope one day we hear from Dr Hodeige, Max and Hubert. But what am I, a heroine, or a 'Jerry lover'?"

Jacques thought for a while, "It doesn't really matter what people think, we are just us, and we do what we think is right."

POSTSCRIPT

You may be curious about this story, and would like to know what was real and actually happened. Well, everyone in the story, with one exception, really did exist, and most of the events took place in exactly the way described.

I, myself, was Marianne, and a boy who became a friend was sent from France to live with a relative who lived next door, because his parents thought the island would be a place of refuge throughout the war. When German forces occupied the island our lives, and the lives of everyone, were transformed.

People In The Story.

The names of most the people in the story have been changed to give anonymity.

However, some individual names have not been changed, because I owe a great debt of gratitude to them: Grandparents Renouf and Camp, Horace Camp, Madam De La Rosa, Madam Marie Helene, Bill Green, Reg Blanchford, Mrs Druet, Stan Workman, Dr Rose, Max the medical orderly, Dr. Hans Hodeige and Huburt Anton Schulz,

The story ended with Liberation, but there are some facts, which may be of interest.

G.U.N.S. Guernsey Underground News Service. For nearly two years a daily bulletin of the B.B.C. News was produced, and it was estimated that it was read by approximately 300 people.
This was active resistance against the Germans and carried a great risk

In 1944 the Germans discovered, through an informer, the names of the men producing the paper. Charles Machon who started the paper, and printed it, was cruelly treated by the Gestapo, and died in prison in Germany. The others Frank Falla, Joseph Gillingham, Cecil Duquemin, and Ernest Legg were sentenced to imprisonment, and suffered greatly in German prisons, where Joseph Gillingham died.

Miss Sanders: I never saw her again after I left the Convent. However, if she was writing about me she would probably have said, 'she is a very annoying child, often disobedient, never stops chattering, much too big for her boots'. Yet interestingly I have met people who remember her with affection.

Lesley: I didn't see her again after I went to the school in town because she moved away from the parish. I don't know why her family disliked us so much; perhaps there was some feud of which I was unaware. She was the only person who called us 'Jerry Lovers,' and it is that memory that slightly mars the joy of Liberation.

Max: I last saw Max in the back of a British lorry with his comrades, who were then prisoners of war. They were singing 'Lilli Marlene' as they drove down the Ville Au Roi, and when he saw me he gave a wave, and I waved back. I know by 1948 he had returned to Germany, but don't know if Freyda survived the war.

Dr. Hans Hodeige: My memory of seeing him is very clear, wearing black boots and a smart black uniform as worn by the Gestapo but as they were not present on the island, this memory was thought to be false. However it was later corroborated by an inhabitant on the Island of Sark where the Doctor was stationed prior to coming to Guernsey. It transpired that he must have been in the Tank Corp, who were present in the Channel Islands, and who had a choice of uniforms, including black. I believe he saved my Mother's life, and she certainly did feel indebted to him.

However, he is a man of mystery. I talked to Reg Blanchford, the Head of St. John's Ambulance Service, who believed that he had met him, and said he thought he was very arrogant, a typical Nazi. I was certainly intimidated by him, and tried to be invisible when he was around.

At one time he was the army Doctor on the island of Sark. From Guernsey he went to Alderney where there were four camps: Helgoland, Borkum, Nordeney and Sylt, which was the only concentration camp on British soil.

There were over twenty-seven nationalities among the workers; some were from the Organisation Todt, who were German, and foreign men who were civilians, and received payment for construction work.

The remainder were forced labourers known by civilians as slave workers. They included Ukranians, Russians, Poles and Jews who were regarded as sub-human, and even more badly treated than other workers. There are reports of much cruelty on the island, and many, many deaths. These, were usually, recorded as heart failure by the S.S. guards, who wrote and issued the certificates, which were then signed by Dr. Hodeige, even though he never saw the bodies.

I met Daphne Pope, who was one of very few civilians in Alderney during the war, who knew Dr. Hodeige well. She said he was a typical Germanic officer, a Nazi to his toenails, however, she did say that he worked hard as a doctor, and told one story to demonstrate his compassion.

'One day there was a commotion outside the hospital for Germans and some workers. A Russian prisoner, who was not entitled to care from the doctor, was shouting, and trying to enter the hospital. The German guards were yelling, beating him, and trying to drag him away. Dr. Hodeige came out, and to the disgust of the guards took him inside.

When the Russian came out his leg was bandaged, and he said to Mrs Pope, "The doctor asked me to sit on a chair and he knelt down and treated my sores and ulcers. Imagine him kneeling in front of me, a Russian, when I would have expected a German to beat me to death." After the war Dr Hodeige's role as island doctor was investigated, and no evidence of brutality was found against him.

We know a little about him from letters he wrote to my mother, of which a few exist.

For example: February 1944

Dear Mrs Renouff, wat a long time you had not any message from me. It is so stormy weather that no boat was going, and I have a lot of work that time for writing is really short. Alderney is a bad place, no doubt whatever, but it is no worse (what follows next is unclear.) For my own work I have much work- male and female patients,-so I have to race all the day. Compared with Guernsey it is not so plenty time for reading and sleeping. I phoned with Mr. Max and he told me of you being sick. Is it true? What a pity I cannot help you. So I have only the familiarity of sending you a bottle of wine, I wish you will recover quicker and I hope you will enjoy a little. I had not any mail, so I cannot tell you any of the latest news around the world. How is your little daughter and your husband? I think sometimes of your nice company and the first week I missed your house keeping very much. With my best wishes for all of you,
Your Doctor.

January 28 1945 (the war is coming to the end)

My dear Mrs Renouff, first of all I hope you will be healthey in this year as you have in the past----and you feel strong enough to resist all the trammels of this life, as everybody must do. Max told me you require the medicine, and today I send it to you. I was so happy with my flowers last time, and it is a pity I cannot get any here. I hope spring is very early this year. And this bleak and cold island will be a little more friendly.

I believe my family are well as I can say of the news I have got, I could not get any medicine for your little daughter, our dentist has nothing for this purpose. Try to find out a way to get this in Guernsey. It is so important for such a little girl.

I am well and healthy and try to make the best of my lonely life. Lots of work I have to do and I sleep alone as I used to say.

With best wishes to you, your husband and Marilene,

I am Your Doctor.

[I think the reference to medicine was for my mouth ulcers.]

The final letter we received was headed; Dr. Med. Dr. Hans-Joachim Hodeige, which would seem to indicate that he was practising medicine in Germany.

Dated Xmas 1948.

My dear Mrs Renouff, my silence has been due to many domestic problems.

This holiday I am thinking of you and Marilene and wishing you all the best for the New Year. Let's hope there will be peace to us and peoples all over the world and begin to love each other – rather than to proclaim hate and foolish violence. I feel quite well. Some days ago

I met Max; we both have been talking a lot of those days we meet each other. To life,
Sincerely, Your Doctor.

So enemy or friend? I don't know, but I thank him with all my heart.

Dr. Hodeige on the island of Alderney, no longer wearing the black uniform.

Huburt Anton Shulz: This is the German whose photograph is on the back cover and on page 158. He was the man who gave me bread when he was starving, and who took my father fishing with a hand grenade at Saint's Bay.

I was able to obtain the name of his commanding officer in Guernsey, and wrote to him asking questions relating to Huburt, and give some of his answers.